EXPLORING THE
ATMOSPHERE

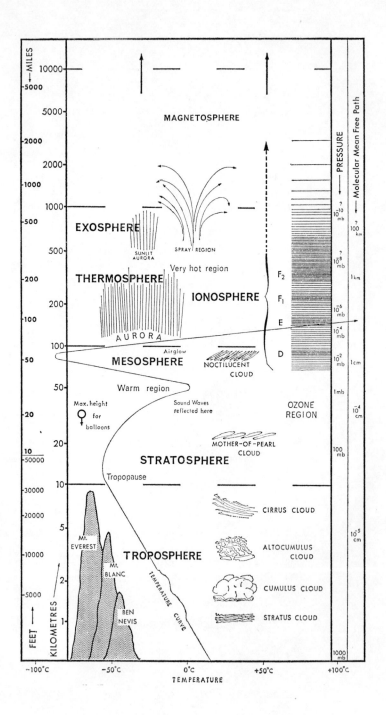

EXPLORING THE ATMOSPHERE

G. M. B. DOBSON
D.Sc., C.B.E., F.R.S.

Formerly Reader in Meteorology
University of Oxford

SECOND EDITION

OXFORD
AT THE CLARENDON PRESS
1968

Oxford University Press, Ely House, London W. 1

GLASGOW NEW YORK TORONTO MELBOURNE WELLINGTON
CAPE TOWN SALISBURY IBADAN NAIROBI LUSAKA ADDIS ABABA
BOMBAY CALCUTTA MADRAS KARACHI LAHORE DACCA
KUALA LUMPUR SINGAPORE HONG KONG TOKYO

FIRST EDITION 1963
SECOND EDITION 1968

PRINTED IN GREAT BRITAIN

TO
O. M. D.

Preface to the Second Edition

THE International Geophysical Year of 1957–8 (a year of maximum solar activity) was so successful that the co-operative effort was continued in 1959 and a further international year was arranged for 1964–5 which was a period of minimum solar activity. As a result of all this international research a great deal of new knowledge has become available since this book was first written in 1962. With the issue of a second edition the opportunity has been taken to incorporate much of this new knowledge and in particular a new chapter has been added on the magnetosphere, a subject about which hardly anything was known five years ago.

G. M. B. D.

Watch Hill
The Ridings
Shotover
Oxford
1967

Preface to the First Edition

THE period July 1957 to December 1958 was designated an International Geophysical 'Year', and during this time a special effort was made to obtain simultaneous observations of many geophysical phenomena at places all over the world and particularly at those places where such observations had, up to then, been scarce. By a remarkable international effort the I.G.Y. proved a great success and much new knowledge was obtained. During question time, after some semi-popular lectures on the atmosphere in connection with the I.G.Y., inquiries were made for the names of books on geophysical subjects, which were suitable for the non-specialist who was interested in researches on the atmosphere. Now that many new facts have come to light through the activities of the I.G.Y., the present seems a suitable time to give an account of geophysical research, for which there seemed to be a demand.

The present book is not one for the specialist; it is not a comprehensive account of meteorology or geophysics. It consists rather of a number of chapters each devoted to describing the present knowledge and current research in a number of departments into which the study of the atmosphere naturally falls. The subjects which have been selected are those of which an account can more easily be given in non-technical terms and which are of particular interest, in that they are in a state of active development and much research is being carried out on them at the present time. This last condition naturally implies that our knowledge is rapidly increasing, with new facts continually being discovered, and many theories are in a state of flux and are changing all the time, but this disadvantage is far outweighed by the fact that the subjects are vitally alive.

The question of units of temperature and height which should be used, is a very difficult one and has been very carefully considered. Those readers who have some scientific knowledge will be used to thinking in degrees centigrade and metres. It is realized that there will be others who would prefer degrees fahrenheit and feet or miles. The practice of giving both units every time was generally condemned as causing an undesirable break in the reading. Since the continental units are being more and more employed in English-speaking countries, it was decided to use them in this book, particularly since the British Meteorological Office now gives temperatures in degrees centigrade in the daily weather forecasts. Tables of equivalents are given for those who desire them.

I am very greatly indebted to several friends who have very kindly read the typescript and made valuable suggestions. I should also like to thank the staff of the Clarendon Press for help in the production of this book.

G. M. B. D.

Watch Hill
Shotover
Oxford

Contents

1. A General Picture of the Atmosphere

I. INTRODUCTION

IN this chapter it is proposed to give a general, but very brief account of the characteristics of the atmosphere as a whole, so that the reader who comes new to the subject may get a comprehensive picture of those phenomena that will be discussed more fully in their turn in later chapters.

Nomenclature of the Upper Atmosphere

Those who have studied books on the upper atmosphere, from both sides of the Atlantic, may well be confused by a superabundance of names that have been suggested for the different regions of the atmosphere. At the present time the nomenclature is by no means settled and in different countries two different names may be used for the same region of the atmosphere. While an agreed system of names is useful, the reader would do well to concentrate primarily on the physical properties of the different parts of the atmosphere, since mere names add nothing to the real understanding of the subject. The names shown in the frontispiece are in fairly general use, at least in Europe.

2. THE FRONTISPIECE

The frontispiece has been drawn to show pictorially the general characteristics of the atmosphere at the different levels and the heights of the various phenomena that will be discussed in this book. In such a picture it is not possible to represent the heights of the different phenomena with great accuracy; moreover there are often large changes with season and with latitude and only mean values can be given. In the diagram the height scale is not uniform, but contracts upwards, since otherwise the diagram would be unduly large.† In addition to indicating the heights of the various phenomena, a curve is given showing the general temperature of the air at different heights, while at the side of the diagram, scales show the pressure of the air and the mean free path of the molecules (or the distance that they travel between collisions with other molecules). We now turn to discuss very briefly the various characteristics of the atmosphere.

3. THE TEMPERATURE OF THE AIR

The changes of temperature with height in the atmosphere are very remarkable; there are three warm regions in the atmosphere separated by two cold regions. As will be seen from the curve of temperature in the frontispiece, warm regions are found: (*a*) near the surface of the earth; (*b*) at a height of some 40 to 60 km; (*c*) right at the top of the atmosphere, above about 150 km. Between these warm regions are cold regions, the lower extending from about 10 to 35 km and the upper one around 80 to 90 km, the exact heights depending on the latitude. Most of our knowledge of the temperature of the air up to heights of 20 or 30 km has been obtained by sending up instruments on small free balloons, which measure the temperature and pressure of the air through which they rise. At the present time almost all instruments contain small radio transmitters, which send down signals indicating the temperature and pressure of the air.

The general distribution of temperature with height that is shown in the frontispiece is true for middle latitudes, but this general type of distribution is found all over the world (except sometimes in the polar winter) though the absolute values may differ from place to place and from time to time. At some height, shown in the diagram as about 10 km, the temperature suddenly ceases to fall with increasing height; this level is known as the tropopause, while the region between this and the ground is known as the troposphere, the region immediately above the tropopause being known as the stratosphere.

By the first decade of the twentieth century the existence of the troposphere and stratosphere had become well established,

† The height scale is logarithmic except for the lowest kilometre.

but a surprise came in the 1920s, when observations of meteors first showed that the air at a height of about 50 km was as warm as that at ground level. The existence of this warm region was soon confirmed by observations of sound waves, and later by observations from rockets. Much less is known about the cold region at a height of 80 to 90 km or about the very hot region above 150 km. Evidence for the high temperature above 150 km comes partly from radio measurements and more recently and much more fully from rockets and satellites.

4. ATMOSPHERIC PRESSURE

The pressure of the air at any level in the atmosphere is due to the weight of air above that level, while the difference of the pressures at two levels is due to the weight of air in the region between the two levels. The percentage difference of pressure between two levels depends only on the temperature and composition of the air and, since there is little difference in the proportions of the different gases in the atmosphere below a height of 100 km, the rate of fall of pressure with height depends primarily on the temperature of the air, when the temperature is high, the pressure falls slowly with increasing height and vice versa.

A scale at the side of the frontispiece gives the average pressure at different heights in millibars (mb), where 1000 mb is approximately the average pressure at sea level. Up to a height of about 30 km these values are fairly accurately known and there is no great uncertainty up to 50 km. Above this level the possible errors are larger, while above 100 km they may be quite large. If we know the temperature and composition of the air at all heights, it is easy to calculate the pressure or density at any level but, unfortunately, at very great heights it is not easy to measure the temperature directly and frequently we must work the other way round and, from the best measurements of pressure or density as obtained from rockets or satellites, we calculate the temperature of the air. It is of interest to note that at heights above 100 km the pressure is so low that it would normally be regarded as a vacuum, yet we must regard the earth's atmosphere as extending to a height of at least 1000 km, while the earth's magnetic field is responsible for producing

the belt of electrons that circulate round the earth at a distance
of some four times the radius of the earth.

5. THE OZONE-RICH REGION

There is a very small amount of ozone in the atmosphere, less
than one part in a million of all the other gases, and this is
mainly situated at a great height above the surface, yet no other
atmospheric gas has been studied in so much detail as ozone.
(Ozone is a form of oxygen which has three atoms in its molecule in contrast to ordinary oxygen which has only two atoms
in its molecule.) Daily measurements of the amount of ozone
in the atmosphere have been made for many years at places
scattered all over the world—particularly during the International Geophysical Year. The full reasons for the great
interest in this rather rare gas will become clear in Chapter 6,
which is devoted to this special subject. It is enough to say here
that much of its importance lies in the fact that it is very opaque
to ultra-violet light, and its absorption of solar ultra-violet light
gives rise to the warm region at a height of about 50 km. Ozone
is also of interest because its amount varies from day to day and
from place to place and, although it is situated high in the
atmosphere, these variations are closely associated with changes
in the weather. Ozone has also been studied because it can be
used to trace large-scale movements of the air at high levels.

6. UNUSUALLY HIGH CLOUDS

Almost all normal clouds occur in the troposphere, but on
rather rare occasions clouds may be seen at heights of about
27 km and on other rare occasions at heights of about 85 km.
These clouds are only seen after sunset (or before sunrise) when
the clouds of the troposphere are in the earth's shadow, while
the high clouds are still lit by the setting (or rising) sun. The
clouds at a height of 27 km show strong iridescent colours and
are, in consequence, known as mother-of-pearl clouds. It is not
yet known why these clouds should appear only within a rather
narrow range of heights around 27 km. The higher clouds, often
known as noctilucent clouds, are also of unknown origin and
it is not even certain whether they are composed of ice crystals

or of dust, but they seem to be associated with the very low temperature at this level.

7. THE AURORA

The aurora is one of the most spectacular phenomena in the atmosphere and its light is emitted by the air at heights of between 100 and 400 km. In certain circumstances, which will be discussed in Chapter 9, it may extend as high as 1000 km. Most of the light is emitted by the air when it is bombarded by electrically charged particles travelling at very high speeds. These particles are shot out from the sun and we shall see later that the aurora, disturbances of the earth's magnetic field, and changes in the ionosphere are all closely connected with sunspots and other solar phenomena.

8. ELECTRICAL PHENOMENA IN THE ATMOSPHERE

A. *Phenomena in the Troposphere*

(i) *Thunderstorms*

Thunder clouds are very deep and generally extend through nearly the whole of the troposphere. We shall see in Chapter 5 that electrical potentials exceeding several million volts are found in thunderstorms, while the current in lightning flashes is measured in thousands and ten thousands of amperes. Although the nature of the electrical 'machine' which generates the electricity in thunderstorms is still not known with certainty, much has been found out about lightning flashes which is of great interest.

(ii) *Fine weather electricity*

Cosmic radiation and radioactive matter make the air at all heights a slight conductor of electricity, and even during fine weather there is a minute electric current flowing down from the air into the ground. The origin of this current was for a long time a subject of much discussion, but it now seems fairly certain that thunderstorms charge up the lower levels of the ionosphere and that the charge spreads out, through the ionosphere, all over the world and slowly flows back to the ground through the air.

B. *The Ionosphere*

While all the air in the atmosphere is a slight conductor of electricity, the conductivity of the air above about 80 km is very much greater than that in the lower regions, particularly during the day-time. This region is known as the ionosphere, and is of great importance in the propagation of radio waves to distant parts of the world. Further, it is in these regions that the electric currents flow that cause the daily variations of the earth's magnetic field that we shall discuss in Chapter 10. The variations in the conductivity of the ionosphere are closely associated with conditions on the sun. Four separate levels of the ionosphere can be distinguished and are known as the D, E, F_1, and F_2 regions, the D region being at a height of about 70 to 80 km and the F_2 region 300 to 400 km.

C. *The Magnetosphere and Van Allen Belts*

The magnetic field of the earth extends out to a great distance and, although it is very weak in these outer regions, it interacts with the charged particles that are continually being shot out from the sun—the so-called solar wind. The interaction with the solar wind produces a fairly definite limit to the region affected by the earth's magnetic field. This limit is known as the magnetopause, and the region within the magnetopause, where the earth's magnetic field is effective, is known as the magnetosphere. Actually it is not a sphere, but extends towards the sun to a distance equal to about ten times the earth's radius, while in the opposite direction it extends to a much greater distance and is known as the earth's magnetic tail.

Within the magnetosphere there are two belts which surround the earth and contain large numbers of electrically charged particles. These are known as the inner and outer Van Allen belts and are situated roughly 3000 and 15 000 km above the earth.

9. THE 'TOP' OF THE ATMOSPHERE

In this brief review of the atmosphere we have passed upwards from the ground to a height of some 500 km where, apart from exceptional cases, even the aurora is left behind and only the magnetosphere which, perhaps, should not be regarded as part

of the atmosphere—lies at still greater altitudes. It may, however, be asked what exactly happens at the very outside of the
atmosphere? What is the 'top' of the atmosphere? How high
does the atmosphere extend? While there is no simple answer
to the latter question, it will be of interest to consider the conditions at these great heights. First, however, it may be useful to
some readers if we digress for a moment for a short discussion
about atoms and molecules.

A gas consists of a very large number of unit particles which
are extremely small and are all moving about at high speeds in
random directions. In some gases, such as argon and helium
the unit particles are single atoms. In other gases, such as
oxygen and nitrogen, the atoms are associated in pairs, when
they are known as molecules. In such gases the molecule is the
unit particle. In yet other gases such as ozone, three atoms are
grouped together in the molecule. Water vapour and carbon
dioxide, being chemical compounds, also have three atoms in
their molecules. The number of molecules in a cubic centimetre
of a gas under normal conditions is very great indeed, exceeding one with nineteen noughts after it. The speed with which
molecules move is of the order of 2000 km/h and increases as the
gas becomes hotter. All the molecules, of whatever molecular
weight, in any given volume of gas have the same average kinetic
energy (i.e. energy of movement) though there will be differences
between one molecule and another. In gases with light molecules
e.g. helium, the molecules move much faster than in gases with
heavy molecules, such as carbon dioxide, even though the
molecules are all mixed together. The temperature of a gas
depends on the average kinetic energy of its molecules. Naturally
the molecules are continually colliding with each other and, in
the air near ground level, they make more than a thousand
million collisions per second. The average distance which a
molecule travels between two collisions varies with the size of
the molecule and the number present and is known as the mean
free path. In the lowest atmosphere the mean free path is less
than 1/10 000 cm but, as indicated in the frontispiece, it increases
to several kilometres in the rare upper atmosphere. The pressure
of a gas on the walls of a vessel containing it is due to the myriads
of impacts of these minute molecules as they strike and rebound
from the walls.

To return to the conditions in the upper atmosphere; during the time that a molecule is travelling freely between two collisions it will be subject to gravity and will fall downwards in the same way as any larger body, but when the mean free path is very small and the time between collisions is very short, the change of velocity under the action of gravity will also be very small. It has already been noted that the mean free path increases with increasing height, and when we get to heights where the mean free path is several kilometres long, it will occasionally happen that a molecule rebounds upwards after a collision and may encounter no other molecule until it has travelled several kilometres. The further it travels upwards, the less likely it is to encounter another molecule. In such conditions the action of gravity will be marked and will slow down the upward velocity of the molecule until it finally begins to fall back to earth. At still greater heights, most of the upward moving molecules will have very long mean free paths and will be moving freely under the action of gravity; indeed the molecules may be thought of as very similar to a spray from a jet of water, in which the individual droplets move upwards in random directions and fall back to the ground. This region of the atmosphere is therefore sometimes known as the spray region though also known as the exosphere. The height of the beginning of the exosphere or spray region is now thought to be at a height of between 600 and 800 km. Much of the spray region consists of free oxygen atoms, while at very great heights, above about 1500 km, hydrogen atoms may predominate, though at such heights the number of molecules per cubic centimetre is only of the order of a hundred thousand—a very small number compared with that near the ground.

The top of this spray region, which is the top of the atmosphere, is quite indefinite since a few fast-moving light molecules may travel up to very great heights before they fall back into the denser region of the atmosphere. Some light molecules, such as hydrogen or helium, at the high temperature of the uppermost atmosphere will be able to leave the atmosphere and the gravitational influence of the earth. (See later under helium.)

It is now believed that the solar corona (see Chapter 7) extends, as outward streaming hydrogen atoms and electrons, well beyond the earth, so that interplanetary space is not empty, and indeed the outer atmosphere of the earth merges into inter-planetary space without any definite boundary. Various estimates of the number of atoms in interplanetary space put the number between 10 and 1000 per cubic centimetre. It may be of interest to mention that interstellar space (i.e. space within our galaxy, between the stars) may contain some ten molecules per cubic centimetre, while intergalactic space (i.e. the outer space between the galaxies) may contain one molecule per cubic centimetre.

10. COMPOSITION OF THE AIR

The composition of the atmosphere will be discussed here in rather more detail than other points since it will not be treated again later. The air near the ground, and even up to heights of 50 km or more, is remarkably uniform in composition apart from a few special gases such as water vapour and ozone. Table 1.1 gives the proportions of the non-varying gases. Since

TABLE 1.1. *Proportions of Gases in the Atmosphere*

Gas	Proportion by volume		Relative thickness	
Total	100	per cent	8·0	km
Nitrogen	78·1	per cent	6·25	km
Oxygen	20·9	per cent	1·68	km
Argon	0·9	per cent	74	m
Carbon dioxide	0·033	per cent	2·6	m
Neon	18	parts per million	15	cm
Helium	5	parts per million	4	cm
Methane	2	parts per million	1·6	cm
Krypton+zenon	1	part per million	8	mm
Hydrogen	0·5	part per million	4	mm
Nitrous oxide	0·5	part per million	4	mm

it is difficult to appreciate figures such as those given in column 2, column 3 has been added to show the proportions in another way, which can be explained as follows: if all the air in the atmosphere were contained in a uniform layer of constant density at all heights and equal to the normal density at ground level, then the atmosphere would have a sharp top at a height of 8 km. For the purpose of Table 1.1, the gases of the atmosphere are supposed to be separated out into their different layers, each layer containing only nitrogen, only oxygen, only argon, etc., so that the total thickness of all the layers makes up the 8 km referred to above.

Composition of the atmosphere in great heights

Table 1.1 gives the composition of the air near the ground. If the atmosphere were entirely quiescent and stagnant, the heavier gases would concentrate under gravity in the lower levels while the lighter gases would be more uniformly distributed in height. There would, therefore be a change in the composition with height. In the lower atmosphere, however, there is so much mixing that no certain evidence of an increase in the proportion of the lighter gases has ever been obtained below 100 km. Some years ago it was thought that the stratosphere would be stagnant enough for separation of the heavy and light gases to take place, but it is now known that the proportions are constant up to much greater heights. The earliest measurements made with the object of detecting changes in the proportion of the different gases at great heights used evacuated vessels sent up on rockets. The vessels were opened and closed again near the top of the flight and the samples of air so obtained were analysed when they were recovered. There was, however, always some doubt whether a true sample of the air at the high level was obtained by this method. More recently analyses of the air have been made on the rocket itself by the use of a mass spectrograph, in which the different atoms and molecules are separated out and their relative amounts measured. The apparatus is freely exposed on the nose of the rocket so that it should get a true sample of the air, unaffected by the presence of the rocket. The results are transmitted to the ground by radio. The measurements that have been made up to the present time indicate that while molecular oxygen and nitrogen predominate below 100 km, oxygen begins to be dissociated into individual atoms above this level and most of the oxygen is dissociated above about 120 km, so that the atmosphere is largely atomic oxygen and molecular nitrogen between about 200 and 500 km. Above about 600 km helium—being much lighter— may be the predominant gas, while at much greater heights the outer atmosphere may be largely hydrogen. Nitrogen is not easily dissociated by the sun's ultra-violet light so that it is largely in the molecular form up to at least 200 km.

II. NOTES ON THE GASES OF THE ATMOSPHERE

Many of the individual gases which make up the atmosphere have special points of interest about them, and we shall now consider each of the gases in turn.

A. *Nitrogen*

This is much the most abundant gas in the atmosphere but, for the most part, it is chemically inactive and takes no important part in the chemical activities of the atmosphere. Nitrates are a plant food of the first importance, but plants cannot obtain their nitrogen directly from the air, and in natural conditions the nitrogen of the atmosphere is only made available to plants through the action of certain nitrifying bacteria present in the roots of leguminous plants. At the present time very large amounts of nitrogenous fertilizers are made by artificial methods from the nitrogen of the air, but the total amount of nitrogen in the atmosphere is so enormous that the amount used for fertilizers is a very small fraction of the whole, and when plants and animals decay, much of the nitrogen that they contain goes back into the atmosphere.

B. *Oxygen*

It is unnecessary to stress the importance of oxygen for the respiration of all animals and plants and for the combustion of fuel. In view of the importance of oxygen for all life and for combustion, it is interesting to note that the earth is exceptional among the planets in having an appreciable amount of oxygen in its atmosphere. The atmospheres of the other inner planets consist mainly of methane or carbon dioxide.

Both nitrogen and oxygen are nearly transparent to the in-coming radiation from the sun and also to the outgoing radiation from the earth and the atmosphere (see Chapter 3). However, oxygen does absorb extremely short-wave, ultra-violet, and X-ray radiation from the sun at a high level in the atmosphere and this is partly responsible for the formation of an electrically conducting layer—the ionosphere. Absorption by oxygen of longer ultra-violet solar radiation splits the two atoms associated in a molecule of oxygen into single atoms. These single atoms may combine with an oxygen molecule to give a molecule of ozone. It is in this way that the ozone in the upper atmosphere is formed.

c. *Carbon Dioxide*

Though this gas is only present to the extent of three parts in ten thousand, it is of great importance in two ways. First, green plants obtain the whole of the carbon in their tissues from the carbon dioxide in the air, through the action of sunlight on the chlorophyll which they contain. Owing to the small concentration of carbon dioxide in the atmosphere, a very large amount of air must come into contact with the chlorophyll of the plant. If the leaves of a plant could extract the whole of the carbon dioxide from the air with which they came in contact, they would require 100 000 ft^3 of air to form 1 lb of carbon in their tissues. It is estimated that, on the average, any molecule of carbon dioxide in the atmosphere is taken up by a plant, and given off again when the plant decays, once in every 10 to 30 years.

Second, carbon dioxide is fairly transparent to most of the solar radiation passing downwards through the atmosphere to the ground, but it strongly absorbs some of the radiation passing outwards from the earth to space. It will be seen in Chapter 3 that this is of importance in determining the temperature of some of the layers of the upper atmosphere.

It is clear that there have been changes in the proportion of carbon dioxide in the atmosphere within geological time, but at the present time the amount is rather constant, both with time and with place. Though forest fires and the combustion of coal adds large amounts of carbon dioxide to the atmosphere, the variations are usually not more than 5 per cent either way. The oceans, by the formation of carbonates and bicarbonates, take up large amounts of carbon dioxide, the amount depending on the temperature. The carbon dioxide in the oceans is many times as great as that in the atmosphere and it is a disputed point how far the oceans keep the amount of carbon dioxide in the atmosphere constant. Some extensive measurements made during the International Geophysical Year have indicated that in the northern hemisphere there is a fairly regular annual variation in the amount of atmospheric carbon dioxide of about five parts in a million, the maximum being in spring and the minimun in autumn. No such annual variation was found in the southern hemisphere. It has been suggested that the variation is due to the action of plants in taking up carbon dioxide during the growing season.

Carbon dioxide plays an important part in a method of dating organic fossils up to some 20 000 years old, which may be worth mentioning here. Normal carbon (atomic weight 12) is a stable element, but there is another isotope of carbon (atomic weight 14) usually called radio-carbon, which is radioactive. When cosmic radiation (see Chapter 5) enters the upper atmosphere from outer space it produces neutrons, and if one of these neutrons strikes an atom of nitrogen (atomic weight 14) in the atmosphere it may enter its nucleus and if so a proton (with one positive charge) is immediately ejected from the nucleus. Thus, while the mass of the nucleus remains unchanged, its positive charge is reduced by one unit and the nitrogen atom is changed into a carbon atom, with all the chemical properties of a normal carbon atom, but having an atomic weight of 14. Since this new type of carbon atom is radioactive, after existing for some time as a carbon atom it suddenly ejects an electron, thus increasing the positive charge on the nucleus by one unit and the atom again becomes a normal atom of nitrogen. The average lifetime of the radioactive carbon atom is 5700 years. The radio-carbon formed in the upper atmosphere becomes radio-carbon dioxide and is gradually mixed throughout the whole atmosphere. Thus radio-carbon dioxide is always being slowly formed and is also slowly disintegrating, and after a sufficient time the amount in the atmosphere will be in equilibrium, when the rate of formation will be equal to the rate of disintegration. With the present intensity of cosmic radiation there is an equilibrium when there is one molecule of radio-carbon dioxide to every million million molecules of normal carbon dioxide. There is no reason to expect that this ratio has changed much within the last 100 000 years. Provided that green plants take up carbon from radio-carbon dioxide just as they do from normal carbon dioxide (and about this there is still some discussion), then for every million million atoms of carbon in the tissues of a growing plant we may expect to find one atom of radio-carbon. However, the radio-carbon immediately begins to revert back to nitrogen and if we dig up a tree stump, for example, which has been buried in a bog for 5700 years, then half the radio-carbon will have changed back to nitrogen and there will be only one atom of radio-carbon to every two million million atoms of normal carbon. One part in a million million is a very small quantity to measure but fortunately there are very sensitive methods available for measuring the amounts of radioactive materials, for example the Geiger counter, which counts individual particles ejected from disintegrating radioactive atoms. Tests made on timber whose age is known historically, indicate that there have been periods of some centuries when the proportion of radioactive carbon dioxide was slightly greater, and other periods when it was slightly less, than the average. This may be due to variations in the intensity of cosmic radiation entering the atmosphere. During the last century or so, the increase in the amount of coal burnt appears to have led to a fall in the proportion of radioactive to normal carbon dioxide in the atmosphere, since most of the radioactive carbon in coal will long ago have disintegrated. Quite recently atomic explosions have caused an increase in the amount of radioactive carbon dioxide.

In general the method of dating by radio-carbon seems to give reliable estimate of the age of fossils up to about 20 000 years.

D. *Helium*

The amount of helium in the atmosphere is extremely small but it is of great interest; indeed, it is the very smallness of the amount which is of interest, since much larger amounts might have been expected. Helium is continually flowing into the atmosphere out of the earth, particularly from oil fields in the United States, and it is estimated that, if there had been no loss of helium from the atmosphere within geological times, there should be about ten times as much helium now in the atmosphere as that actually found. Helium is a chemically inert gas so that it cannot be lost by chemical action and it has been suggested that it may escape into space from the upper limits of the atmosphere.

Under the section The Top of the Atmosphere it has been shown that, at very high levels, the motion of the molecules resembles that of a spray, the individual molecules being shot up to great heights; most of them finally fall back towards the earth. Should the initial speed of a molecule exceed about 11 km/s in its upward flight, it will not fall back to earth, but will continue on upwards into outer space, just as some of the fastest rockets have done. Now the average speed of a molecule of a gas depends not only on the temperature but also on the molecular weight of the gas, light molecules moving faster than heavy ones, so that light gases such as hydrogen and helium will be more likely to escape than heavier gases like oxygen and nitrogen. At the temperature of the lower atmosphere the loss of helium would be negligible but, since the temperature of the uppermost regions is very high, some escape of helium into space will be possible. Before measurements had been made by rockets and satellites, the unexpectedly small amount of helium in the atmosphere had been used as an argument that the temperature at heights of 600 to 700 km must be very high. There is, however, another way in which helium molecules might acquire abnormally high speeds. If the molecule of air with which the helium atom last collided were 'excited' (i.e. if one of its electrons had more than the normal energy) the helium atom might take up this additional energy and rebound with an abnormally high speed.

E. *Neon*

The amount of neon in the atmosphere is nearly as small as that of helium and, to the general reader, its chief interest is probably that this gas, which is used in the bright red 'neon' signs, is obtained from the minute quantity in the atmosphere.

F. *Hydrogen*

Though the amount of hydrogen in the lower atmosphere is negligible, the outermost parts of the atmosphere (probably above about 1500 km height) are thought to consist largely of protons (hydrogen atoms which have lost one electron) and free electrons. This hydrogen is probably mainly formed by the decomposition of water vapour and methane by the ultra-violet radiation in sunlight at lower levels. Since hydrogen is continually lost by escape into space, there must be a continual drift of hydrogen upwards through the upper atmosphere from the levels where it is formed.

2. The Temperature and Humidity of the Troposphere and Stratosphere

I. INTRODUCTION

IN the next two chapters we shall discuss in detail how the remarkable temperature structure of the atmosphere, which was briefly described in the first chapter, has been measured. Different methods must be used to measure the temperature of the air at different heights and it will be convenient to divide this account into two parts. In this chapter we shall discuss the temperature and humidity of the lower levels which can be reached by aircraft and balloons, while in Chapter 3 we shall deal with much higher levels where other methods must be used.

2. TEMPERATURE IN THE REGION BELOW 30 KM

A. *Historical*

The first early measurements begun at the end of the last century were made with instruments carried on balloons, which recorded on a small chart the pressure, the temperature, and the humidity of the air through which they rose. In the British Isles the finances for this work were extremely slender, and only small—and therefore relatively cheap—balloons could be used. An instrument which was very simple and very light was designed by the late W. H. Dines in which the record was scribed by a steel point on a metal plate about an inch square. As a result of the ascents with these simple little instruments a great deal of information about the atmosphere was obtained though the actual discovery of the stratosphere was made on the Continent. It was known that in the lower levels of the atmosphere the temperature fell with increasing height, and it was generally supposed that this fall would continue to the 'top' of the atmosphere. The early measurements showed that so far

C

from this being the case the fall of temperature generally stopped suddenly (within 100 m or so) at some height around 10 to 15 km, and from there upwards it not only ceased to fall but often actually rose—sometimes rising 5 or 10° C by the time the greatest height was reached. This was so surprising that some people refused for a long time to believe the correctness of the measurements.

B. *Modern Instruments*

The early instruments had two serious disadvantages: (i) the instruments had to be found and returned if their information was to be available, and many were never found; (ii) there was necessarily a delay of days, weeks, or sometimes years before the instrument was found. With the advent of radio, it became possible to attach a small radio transmitter to the instrument which would signal to a receiver on the ground the temperature, pressure, and humidity of the air through which it was passing, so that the information was immediately available and it is now of no great importance whether the instrument is found or not. Since about 1940 all upper air measurements have been made using radio methods for transmitting the data. Such instruments are usually known as radio-sondes. Various methods can be used for transmitting the information; in one type of instrument an audible note is transmitted whose pitch varies with the temperature, pressure, or humidity. In another type pairs of 'pips' are transmitted whose separation in time gives the same information. Yet another instrument gives the information in Morse code, and so on.

In many cases the temperature is measured by a bi-metallic thermometer, while in others a 'thermistor' is used whose electrical resistance varies with the temperature. Thermistors can be made very small so that they respond quickly to changes of temperature. The pressure is generally measured by an aneroid diaphragm, but at great heights, where the changes of pressure with height is very small, the errors may be serious. Hypsometers are sometimes used, in which the temperature of a liquid boiling under atmospheric pressure gives a measure of the pressure. They have the advantage that they give more accurate readings when the pressure is very low. The measurement of the humidity will be discussed in the section on Humidity.

At the present time routine measurements by balloons reach heights of about 20 to 30 km, though specially large and therefore more expensive balloons may go higher before they burst. A method is now coming into use whereby the instrument is carried up on a small rocket to a height of about 70 km and there released, when it descends on a large parachute, making measurements on the way down. As the large parachute, which is necessary to give a suitable rate of fall at great heights, would fall too slowly at lower levels, this is discarded on the way down and a smaller one comes into use. Such instruments are sometimes known as drop-sondes.

The information obtained by the instruments carried up on small balloons is of such great importance in forecasting the weather that ascents are now made twice or four times a day at many places in Europe and North America and from the ocean weather ships so that maps can be drawn showing the distribution of temperature, pressure, and wind at various levels in the free atmosphere, in addition to those for ground level. The balloon drifts with the wind and, since it is followed by radar, the height and position of the balloon are known and its drift from minute to minute can be calculated, and hence the velocity of the wind and its direction at every height are obtained as well as the temperature, pressure, and humidity.

c. *Average World-wide Upper Air Temperatures*

Measurements of the temperature of the upper air by means of instruments carried up on small balloons have now been made at a large number of places scattered all over the world. The special effort made during the International Geophysical Year (July 1957 to December 1958) and its successors resulted in measurements being obtained in many places of special interest where observations were lacking previously. This was particularly the case in polar regions where recent measurements have proved to be of great interest. We shall begin by describing the average conditions during the different seasons of the year at different latitudes, and later describe the variations which are found from day to day and which are linked with the changing types of weather.

In Fig. 2.1 we have shown the average upper air temperatures (i) within the tropics, (ii) the summer and winter values for

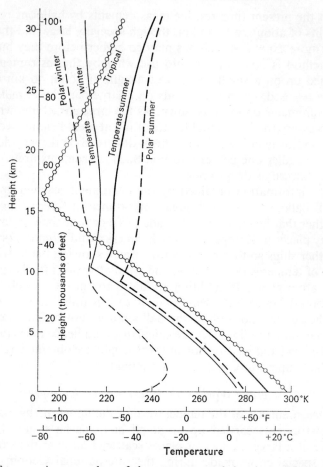

FIG. 2.1. Average values of the temperature of the air at different heights at different seasons.

On individual days the temperature may vary very considerably from these mean values.

middle latitudes, and (iii) the summer and winter values near the poles. The curves bring out several remarkable facts. Except during the winter in high latitudes, the *rate* of fall of temperature with height in the lowest 8 to 10 km of the atmosphere is very similar all over the world and at all seasons. This rate of fall is about 5 to 6° C for every kilometre, being rather faster at high levels than at low levels.

Excepting again the winter in very high latitudes, the fall of temperature comes to an abrupt stop at some level—the tropopause—generally between 7 and 17 km above the earth's surface. Thereafter the curve shows a steady or slowly rising temperature, which continues up to the maximum height reached by balloons. It would appear that the temperature of the air in the troposphere and that in the stratosphere must be controlled by quite different causes. The change from falling to constant or rising temperature at the tropopause frequently takes place quite suddenly—often within a layer only 100 m thick.

The way in which the temperature of the upper air varies with changing latitude depends on the season of the year, but the most outstanding and surprising fact that is shown by Fig. 2.1 is that almost the coldest air anywhere in the lower atmosphere is found over tropical regions at a height of some 17 km. At heights of between 20 and 40 km over polar regions the temperature in winter may be nearly as low as over the equator, but the fraction of the earth's surface over which this cold air is found is small. In the case of the Arctic, there is much variation from day to day and a temperature distribution similar to that of temperate regions is often found, even in winter. In the Antarctic the stratosphere is much more uniformly cold throughout the winter and rises very rapidly in the early summer. It will also be noticed that although the temperature rises rather rapidly above the tropopause within the tropics, yet the air is never as warm as that at corresponding levels in higher latitudes in summer.

The difference between summer and winter temperatures is much greater in the upper stratosphere than in the lower troposphere (apart from a very shallow surface layer near the poles).

The height of the tropopause decreases from the equator towards the poles and there is generally a break about latitude 35° where it suddenly changes height.

In Fig. 2.2 we have shown the distribution of temperature at different latitudes in another way. The figure gives a cross-section of the atmosphere along a meridian from the pole to the equator (neglecting, of course, the curvature of the earth), one half representing the summer hemisphere while the other half represents the winter hemisphere. In order to bring out the main features, the diagram is much simplified, thus for instance, the differences between the northern and southern hemispheres have been neglected. The thin lines are isotherms, or lines of equal temperature, while the thin double line shows the position of the tropopause. The diagram shows the break in the tropopause in latitudes between 30 and 40°. This break may at times be a

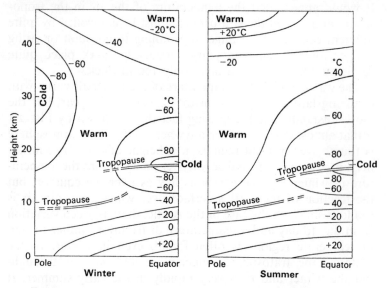

FIG. 2.2. A cross-section of the atmosphere from the pole to the equator showing the general distribution of temperature at different heights in different latitudes in summer and in winter.

Note the very cold air always found at the equatorial tropopause and the cold pool of air over the pole in winter. In both summer and winter there is always warm air at a height of about 50 km at all latitudes.

folding of the tropopause, part of the tropopause being folded back over part of the stratosphere (see Fig. 2.3). A balloon rising here would cross the tropopause at a height of about 12 km and enter air with all the characteristics of the stratosphere, i.e. uniform or rising temperature with height. At some greater height, say 14 km, it would again enter air with the characteristics of the troposphere, i.e. temperature falling with height, and finally at a height of perhaps 16 km it would again enter the stratosphere. It will be seen in Chapter 6 that the concentration of ozone in stratospheric air is much greater than in tropospheric air. When instruments which measure the concentration of ozone are sent up on balloons in a position such as that represented by *AB* in Fig. 2.3, a high concentration of ozone is found above the first tropopause (shown in the figure at 12 km), but at higher levels, e.g. those shown between 14 and 16 km, low ozone is again found until the balloon reaches

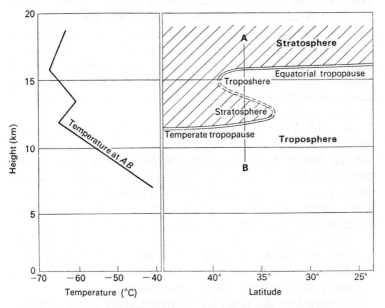

FIG. 2.3. The possible folding of the tropopause in latitudes about 40° Lat.

The temperature distribution at the line *AB* is indicated on the left and the structure of the tropopause on the right. Sometimes there seems to be a break in the tropopause rather than a folding.

the upper tropopause (shown at 16 km), after which high concentrations of ozone are found at all higher levels. This is clear evidence of a 'folding' of the tropopause, giving tropospheric air between an upper and lower layer of stratospheric air.

In Fig. 2.2 the cold area over the winter pole looks as large as that over the tropics, but the area covered by this cold pool is very small compared with that over the tropics since the latter extends right round the world. A second sudden change in the height of the tropopause is also sometimes found about latitude 60°.

Fig. 2.2 shows the *average* distribution of temperature with latitude in the upper atmosphere, but the daily maps of temperature and pressure for a height of 30 km for the whole of the northern hemisphere show how the conditions may vary from place to place. These maps show some very interesting features. The very cold air that is found to the north of about 50° N. in winter results in a low pressure area near the North Pole which persists without much change throughout the winter. This produces a belt of exceptionally strong westerly winds blowing round the pole, the maximum speed being found in latitudes between about 60 and 70° N. This persistent westerly wind may reach speeds of over 200 knots at 30 km and increases still more at greater heights.

The coldest region, and therefore the lowest pressure, is not centred exactly at the North Pole but some 5 to 10° towards Siberia. But perhaps the most unexpected feature shown on these maps for 30 km in winter is an area of warm air and high pressure between Alaska and the Aleutian Island. This produces a very strong pressure gradient and exceptionally strong winds in the stratosphere over Alaska. The reason why there should be this warm, high-pressure area is not understood, though one may suggest that it is in some way connected with the presence of relatively warm Pacific Ocean on the one side of the pole and the very cold land mass on the other side.

In contrast to the rapid fall of temperature and pressure in winter between about 50° N. and the pole, there is little change in either the temperature or the pressure at this level between the equator and 50° N., so that only rather light winds are found in these latitudes.

In March the conditions change completely, the air in high latitudes warms up and the low pressure area near the pole disappears, so that there is little difference in either the temperature or the pressure at a height of 30 km anywhere in the northern hemisphere. As the sun moves north in May the temperature at the North Pole becomes higher than that in any other part of the hemisphere and a centre of high pressure becomes established over the North Pole with easterly winds circulating round it at all latitudes, and there are no irregularities such as the warm, high-pressure centre found over the Aleutian Islands in winter. Moreover, the temperature gradients and pressure gradients are now fairly uniform over the whole of the hemisphere, in contrast to the conditions in winter. These moderate easterly winds continue until August; in September the temperature and pressure gradients again become small in all latitudes until the strong winter-cooling begins in high latitudes and the regular winter regime sets in again.

It is worth while to discuss rather more fully the warming of the stratosphere which takes place each spring in high latitudes. This warming is very curious and its cause is not well understood. The warming generally takes place very suddenly with a rise of temperature of some 10 or more degrees in a few days. This is much too rapid for it to have been caused by the absorption of solar radiation and moreover the warming may take place even before the end of the polar night. Frequently there is a preliminary 'sudden warming' followed by a cooling, after which a second, or even a third warming may occur. These warmings take place any time from January to March. There is evidence that the warming begins high in the stratosphere—possibly at a height of about 50 km—and then spreads to lower levels. It also seems to spread across the polar regions from the Aleutian warm, high pressure area. It would seem that the warming can only be caused by sinking of the air (see Chapter 6).

In the southern hemisphere there have been far fewer measurements at high levels than in the northern hemisphere, partly owing to the fact that the oceans cover so much of the area, but recently there has been great scientific activity in Antarctica and in the next few years our knowledge should greatly increase. So far no abnormality, similar to the Aleutian warm high-pressure area has been found.

The spring warming in Antarctica is notably different from that in the Arctic; only one sudden warming generally occurs and this takes place fairly regularly in October, i.e. much later than that in the northern hemisphere. As in the northern hemisphere, the sudden warming is associated with a sudden increase in the total amount of ozone and again is probably associated with sinking air.

D. *Variations in Upper Air Temperatures from Day to Day*

It must not be supposed that every day on which a balloon is sent up, curves such as those of Fig. 2.1 will be obtained. The conditions vary from one day to another nearly as much as they do between summer and winter. Again the smooth, average curves shown in the figure are often replaced, on individual days, by much more irregular curves with the temperature falling faster or slower at adjacent heights, while not infrequently the temperature may actually rise with height for a few hundred metres, even in the troposphere. These cases of 'inversions' of the normal temperature gradient in the troposphere are commonly found at the tops of cloud sheets and are often associated with very dry air (see section on Humidity).

In middle latitudes striking changes in the whole temperature structure may be found within the course of 2 or 3 days. These changes are associated with a complete alteration of the weather map in the area. One day the surface weather chart may show that a low pressure system covers the country, while the corresponding chart for the upper troposphere will probably show a trough of low pressure extending southwards from a general low-pressure system to the north. Within a day or two, the low pressure system may have moved away and, on the surface weather chart, its place may be taken by a high-pressure area, while the chart for the upper levels shows a ridge of high pressure over the country. Typical curves for the temperature distribution on two such days are shown in Fig. 2.4. On comparing these two curves with those of Fig. 2.1, it will be noticed that the day with high pressure has a curve similar to that for low latitudes, while the day with low pressure has a curve similar to that for high latitudes.

In general, in temperate latitudes it is found that, high pressure, warm troposphere, cold stratosphere, and high tropopause all go together. Similarly, low pressure, cold troposphere, warm stratosphere, and low tropopause go together. In high and low latitudes the connections are less marked.

Up to now we have spoken of the tropopause as if there was always a definite boundary between the troposphere and the stratosphere, but, even apart from the polar winter, there are days on which it is difficult to identify any definite discontinuity. Sometimes the falling temperature of the troposphere may pass gradually into the constant temperature of the stratosphere; on other days there may be two, three, or more changes in the slope of the temperature curve and any of them could be taken as the tropopause. Sometimes there are really two tropopauses such as we have already mentioned as being common in latitudes 30 to 40°.

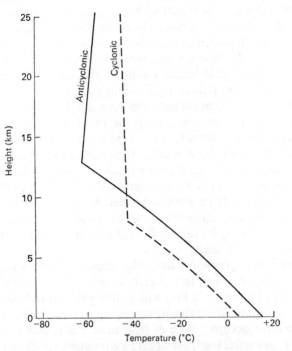

FIG. 2.4. Typical vertical distributions of temperature in middle latitudes on days with cyclonic and anticyclonic pressure distributions.

3. HUMIDITY IN THE TROPOSPHERE AND LOWER STRATOSPHERE

A. *Measurement of Humidity*

The humidity of the air is clearly an important characteristic and we shall see later that it has an unexpected interest in connection with the general circulation of the atmosphere; it is therefore unfortunate that it is difficult to measure the humidity of the air accurately with instruments carried up on small balloons. The difficulty is particularly great in the upper part of the atmosphere where the temperature is very low. The most common method of measuring the humidity in the lower, warmer parts of the atmosphere is to use some substance such as hair or gold-beater's skin, which takes up an amount of water depending on the humidity of the surrounding air and in consequence changes its length with changing humidity, but is little affected by the temperature. The reason for the difficulty at very low temperatures is that there is very little water vapour even in saturated air at these temperatures, so that it takes a long time for the hair or gold-beater's skin to pick up the water that it requires to bring it into equilibrium with the humidity of the surrounding air, hence it becomes exceedingly sluggish in action. (Because of the low vapour pressure of water at these low temperatures it is equally slow in getting rid of its excess water when surrounded by dry air.) At temperatures below $-40°$ C instruments employing these methods are useless. Some idea of the difficulty of making measurements of humidity at these low temperatures will be obtained when it is realized that in the stratosphere the amount of water vapour in several cubic metres of air may be the equivalent of a droplet of water about the size of a pin-head.

Electrical hygrometers have also been used which depend on the change of either the electrical resistance or the dielectric constant of a very thin film which, like gold-beater's skin, takes up water vapour from the air according to the relative humidity.

The most accurate type of hygrometer is probably the dew-point hygrometer (or frost-point hygrometer), which depends on the fact that dew is deposited on a solid surface exposed to the air if the surface is cooled below the temperature at which the air is saturated. Instruments using this principle have been specially designed for work at great heights and can measure the humidity of the air at temperatures as low as $-85°$ C. Unfortunately it is difficult to make instruments of this type which are fully automatic and reliable, and most observations have so far been made by observers in aircraft.

A method which has recently been developed for measuring the small amounts of water vapour in the stratosphere consists in passing the air through a tube, the inside of which is coated with phosphorus pentoxide, which absorbs water vapour very strongly. Two spiral wires are embedded in the same internal surface and an electric potential is applied between them. When the phosphorus pentoxide is dry, no electric current flows between the wires, but when it absorbs water vapour, this is electrolysed to oxygen and hydrogen and the current which flows is a measure of the rate at which water vapour is entering the tube. The apparatus is very suitable for carrying on a small balloon and the results are transmitted to the ground by radio.

Water vapour strongly absorbs certain wavelengths in the infra-red part of the spectrum and measurements of the absorption of sunlight at these wavelengths have been used to measure the total amount of water vapour through which the sunlight has passed. Recent improvements in infra-red techniques, in 'interference' filters and in electronics have made measurements by this method much more accurate.

B. *Results of Measurements of Humidity*

(i) *Humidity in the stratosphere*

Although the existence of the stratosphere had been known from the beginning of the present century, nothing was known about the humidity of the air there, owing to the difficulties of measuring humidity which we have discussed above. Two-seater aircraft, which were able to climb into the stratosphere over England, became available for meteorological research about 1940 and these were fitted with special frost-point hygrometers. Naturally the results of the first observations in the stratosphere were awaited with great interest. Many meteorologists thought that the air would be nearly saturated; the first measurements, however, showed that so far from being saturated, the air was extremely dry. It has now been established that extreme dryness is a characteristic of the air in the lower stratosphere in nearly all places where measurements have been made. The relatively few ascents which have been made up to the present time by the phosphorus pentoxide method and the infra-red method indicate that the stratosphere is dry to at least 30 km. Earlier measurements which had indicated that the humidity was higher at 30 km than at 15 km are now thought to have been affected by water carried up with the apparatus.

As we have just mentioned it was thought many years ago that, since the temperature structure of the stratosphere makes the air at these altitudes very stable, there would be very little mixing up the air, and ordinary molecular diffusion of the gases might be important. In such conditions the water vapour of the upper troposphere would slowly diffuse upwards into the stratosphere and, since the molecular weight of water vapour is little more than half that of air, the amount of water vapour relative to that of air might even increase with height. If the conditions in the stratosphere were really as simple as had been assumed, the air there would certainly have a high relative humidity, and the fact that the air has been found in reality to be very dry leads us to suppose that there is a general circulation of the air between the troposphere and stratosphere; it is now thought that air ascends from the upper troposphere into the stratosphere in very low latitudes and returns from the stratosphere to the troposphere in high and middle latitudes. If such a circulation of air does take place, then the air in the stratosphere would all have had to pass through the very cold region at the top of the troposphere near the equator. While passing through this very cold region, with a temperature of about $-80°$ C, most of the water vapour would condense and fall out of the air as ice crystals, leaving the air with a frost-point of $-80°$ C. That this is really the case is made probable by the fact that this is just about the frost-point of the driest air found in the stratosphere. Further, extensive layers of thin cirro-stratus, such as would be formed by the process suggested, are commonly seen above the equator. The return of air from the stratosphere to the troposphere probably takes place, partly in polar regions —particularly in winter—and partly in cyclonic areas of middle latitudes, very dry air often being found in the upper part of the troposphere in these conditions. We shall have more to say about this when we discuss the ozone in the atmosphere, since ozone measurements also indicate descending air currents in the same regions, as also do the measurements of the 'fall-out' of radioactive matter from thermonuclear explosions (see Chapter 6).

Clouds in the stratosphere. Since the stratosphere is nearly always very dry, one would expect that few, if any, clouds would be formed there. This is indeed the case. Occasionally the tops of very big cumulo-nimbus clouds may rise so violently that they penetrate the tropopause and push up for a kilometre or two into the stratosphere, but otherwise no ordinary clouds are found there. However, in certain special cases clouds may be formed far above the tropopause and are known as mother-of-pearl clouds.

These clouds, which were mentioned in Chapter 1 (section 6), are occasionally seen in rather high, middle latitudes in winter. They are most clearly visible a little after sunset or before sunrise, when they are lit up by the sun but the earth's surface is in darkness. They have now been thoroughly studied and their height has been measured by simultaneous photographs taken at two distant places. They are usually found at a height of about 27 km but may be a kilometre or two above or below this level. Since the air in the stratosphere is normally very dry, the temperature must be very low before any clouds can be formed, but it will be seen from Fig. 2.2 that the temperature is normally very low at these levels in high latitudes in winter. However, the normal low temperature of these regions would not be enough to form the clouds, and it is believed that further cooling is caused by local uplift as the wind blows over mountains. It is known that waves set up when air blows over a mountain range extend to many times the height of the mountains. These clouds often show strong iridescent colours, for which reason they are known as mother-of-pearl clouds.

(ii) *Humidity in relation to clouds*

Up to now we have been discussing the dryness of the air in the stratosphere which seems to be a world-wide phenomenon. We now turn to very much smaller-scale phenomena, namely the humidity near certain types of clouds. A very interesting case is that of stratocumulus cloud in anticyclonic weather. This type of cloud, which may have a thickness of about 200 m is often found at a height of about 2 km as a uniform sheet covering a very wide area of country, and in winter gives very dull weather that may persist for days, yet the cloud may suddenly clear completely leaving cloudless skies, only to return again in, perhaps, a few hours. The division between the cloudy and the clear sky is usually very sudden and the edge of the cloud often shows a cliff-like appearance. The ordinary radio-sonde ascents through this type of cloud showed that there was a rise in temperature and a fall in humidity above the cloud, but could not show the most interesting details which really exist, and only aircraft, fitted with thermometers and dew-point hygrometers, and which can fly in and out of the cloud, can elucidate the details of the temperature and humidity.

Such flights by aircraft have shown that for the first kilometre or so above the ground, where the air was free from cloud, the temperature fell at the rate of about 10° C for every kilometre (i.e. the rate of fall which would occur if the temperature gradient was controlled by mixing of dry air), while the relative humidity increased with height. Within the cloud the rate of fall of temperature was about half this value, corresponding to the rate of fall for mixing of cloudy air. Quite suddenly, at some height about 1500 and 2000 m, the temperature began to rise and rose several degrees in the next few hundred metres while the relative humidity fell to a very low value. The height of this sudden change is usually the height of the top of the cloud. It is remarkable that such dry air should persist for so long, only 100 m or so above the saturated air in the cloud. The reason for this can be seen when it is realized that two different processes are going on at the same time.

(*a*) Within the area covered by an anticyclone there is descending air throughout the troposphere, the air descending at a rate of 10 or 20 m/h. Within the lowest kilometre above the ground, where the frictional effects with the ground are important, the winds blow spirally outwards and so constantly remove air from the centre to the outside of the anticyclone. This removal of air is constantly made good by the descending air from above. The descending air will be warmed by compression and will be very dry.

(*b*) While the dry air from the upper troposphere is continually descending into the lower layers, water is all the time evaporating from the ground, thus supplying water vapour to the lowest air. This damp air is then mixed with air higher up by small-scale turbulence caused by winds, but the amount of this mixing depends very much on the rate of fall of temperature with height: when the temperature falls rapidly with height, then mixing will be rapid, while if the temperature gradient should be reversed, so that the temperature actually rises with height, then mixing in that region will almost cease. In those cases where the fall of temperature continues uninterrupted throughout the troposphere, there will be a steady movement of water vapour upwards, with no accumulation of water vapour at any particular height. If, however, an inversion of temperature gradient should exist at some level where, for 100 m or so, the temperature rises with height, mixing will almost stop and there will be an accumulation of water vapour below this level.

Now these two processes are going on at the same time, water vapour being transported upwards within the lower 1500 to 2000 m and dry air descending into the top of this region. The moist air may, or may not, reach saturation before it is dried by mixing with the descending air; if saturation is reached, then cloud will be formed, while if not reached no cloud will be formed, but the lower boundary of the dry air will be marked by a haze-top. An important point is that the dry air is very much more transparent to long-wave radiation than damp air and the highest 30 m or so of the cloudy layer will be able to radiate fairly freely outwards into space. Whether cloud is formed or not, the top of the damp air will lose much heat by this outward radiation, though, of course, the amount will be greater if cloud is actually formed. This loss of heat maintains the top of the damp region at a lower temperature than that of the air either above or below it; it also helps to maintain the rapid fall of temperature in the layers below it, and therefore to increase the turbulence and the upward diffusion of water vapour. This turbulence produces rather bumpy conditions for the aircraft when flying in it and it is interesting to find that the turbulence continues for about 100 m within the clear air above the cloud top, but above this level the air is very smooth. This shows that water vapour is still being transported upwards within the first 100 m of clear air, but mixing with the dry descending air prevents the formation of cloud. The turbulence cannot penetrate higher because of the great stability of the air at the level where the temperature rises with increasing height.

We can now see why this type of cloud may persist for a long time and then clear completely, since its formation depends on saturation being reached in the damp air before it is mixed too much with the dry descending air. If cloud does form, the outward radiation from the top of the cloud is increased and this in turn increases the cooling and so aids the formation of cloud. The cloud thus tends to form a complete cover or to clear entirely.

3. The Temperature and Density of the Air at Great Heights

I. TEMPERATURE OF THE MIDDLE REGIONS OF THE ATMOSPHERE (30 TO 80 KM)

BY about 1920 our knowledge of the temperature of the atmosphere up to the heights which could be easily reached by small balloons—say 25 km—was fairly good except in the polar regions, but nothing was known about the temperature at greater heights and it was generally assumed that the air remained cold at all higher levels. At this time high-altitude rockets were, of course, unknown and the only way in which some idea of the conditions at these high levels could be obtained was by making use of any natural phenomena which occur at these altitudes, from which the conditions there might be deduced. The study of two phenomena proved useful in this way, namely meteors and the refraction of sound waves. Although these methods are not used today, since far better measurements can be made with the aid of rockets, it may be of interest to describe briefly the way in which the warm region at a height of about 50 km was first discovered.

A. *Results from Meteor Observations*

The first indication that something unexpected was in store came from a study of meteors or 'shooting stars'. Meteorites, which are very bright and occasionally fall to the ground, may be quite large, but the ordinary meteors that are much more common are quite small, usually smaller than a pea. In composition, most meteors are of a stony nature but some are largely composed of iron. The origin of these particles is unknown though many seem to be definitely associated with comets. They have been travelling round the sun, much as comets do, for millions of years at speeds of the order of 50 km/s. Then suddenly, if they strike the earth's atmosphere, they end their career in a streak of light. When this happens, the meteor, in passing through the atmosphere at a very high speed, becomes heated by what we may call 'friction' with the air, and becomes so hot that it begins to evaporate. The little cloud of vapour from the meteor will move forward with the same speed as the meteor, and molecules of vapour will strike molecules of air at such high speeds that light will be produced† and the path of the meteor may become visible. Note, that the meteor itself is too small to be seen, even if it were heated to a temperature far above that at which it evaporates.

Before the meteor can become visible it must be heated to its vaporizing temperature, and this will require a certain amount of heat. As we have said, the heat necessary for this comes from its rapid passage through the air, and the higher the speed of the meteor and the greater the density of the air through which it passes, the greater will be the amount of heat produced. It is this fact, that the heating of meteors depends on the density of the air, which makes it possible to find out something about the density of the atmosphere at the levels where they appear. If the density of the air is low the heating will be small, and the meteor must travel a long distance, or come to lower levels, before it will be heated enough to begin to evaporate. During the time that the meteor is travelling through the air as a visible meteor, it is pouring off vapour as heat flows into it and evaporates the solid particle. The amount of this heat, and therefore the rate at which the meteor evaporates again depends on the density of the air through which it is passing. When all the meteor has evaporated it ceases to be visible. Thus we have the possibility of finding out something about the density of the air both at the height at which the meteor was first seen and that at which it disappeared. We can also find the density of the air if we can measure the rate at which the meteor is slowed down during its visible passage through the atmosphere, but this slowing down of the meteor can only be measured by very careful photographic observations.

In 1922, when the density of the upper air was first calculated from meteor observations, there were no suitable photographic

† For the way in which light is produced by a gas see Chapter 9.

measurements but fortunately many observations had been made by a small group of highly skilled amateur meteor observers of the height, brightness, and speed of many meteors, and these were used for this purpose. Although the measurements were remarkably accurate for eye observations, the densities calculated from these observations showed considerable variations, but the reader can imagine the interest which was aroused when, on first plotting the densities as calculated from the meteor observations against height, it was found that, while the densities for the lower levels were about the expected values, those for the greater heights were larger than expected by about 100 to 1000 times. Fig. 3.1 shows the original plot of the densities of the air as obtained from meteor observations. The line *ABC* gives the density of the air which would be found if the temperature of the air at all heights above the tropopause was $-53°$ C. (The curvature of the line above 100 km is due to an assumption about the separation of heavy and light gases that is now known to be wrong, and should be neglected.) The great interest of the diagram is that all the densities obtained from observations of meteors above 50 km are much greater than those given by the line *ABC*. Though it was known that the possible errors were large, it did not seem likely that the unexpectedly high densities could be accounted for in this way. If the high densities are correct, they could most easily be explained by supposing that the temperature of the air at heights above 50 km was much warmer than $-53°$ C; indeed it appeared to be about the same as at ground level. (The calculation of the temperature from the density is discussed on p. 50.) Since this first estimate of the density of the air at great heights was made, much more work has been done, including observations of meteors by photographic methods; these, and the results recently obtained with the aid of rockets, have now fully confirmed the existence of the warm region at a height of 50 km in widely different parts of the world.

More recently estimates of the temperature of the air have been made from observations of meteors by radar methods. The meteor leaves behind it a trail of ionized air on which radar measurements can be made, signals sent out by a transmitter being reflected back by the conducting meteor trail. From such measurements temperatures have been calculated for the air at

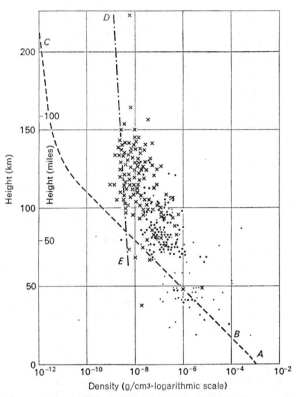

FIG. 3.1. Density of the air as obtained from observations of meteors.

Densities are plotted on a logarithmic scale, the distance between any two vertical lines representing a factor of 100. Each point represents the density as calculated from the observations of one meteor: crosses for the height of appearance; dots for the height of disappearance. The line *ABC* gives the densities which would be found if the temperature of the air was −53° C. (The curved part of the line above 100 km should be neglected.) The line *DE* gives an estimate of the *minimum* possible density of the air as calculated from the observations by another method. This minimum density agrees with the crosses and dots but again indicates a density much greater than that expected if the air temperature was −53° C.

This figure is reproduced by permission of the Royal Society from *Proc. R. Soc.* A **102**, 411 (1922).

heights of about 90 km which agree reasonably well with those obtained by other methods.

The suggestion that there was a warm region at a height of about 50 km as well as the warm region near the ground, with a cold region (the lower stratosphere) between, naturally came as a great surprise and was the subject of much scepticism. Indeed, it seemed almost as absurd as if it had been suggested that, if there were two electrically heated blankets, with an unheated blanket sandwiched between them, the middle blanket would remain permanently cold. However, the reality of the warm region has now been well established by measurements with rockets, and we can satisfactorily explain why the stratosphere remains cold although it is sandwiched between two warm layers. This explanation will be given later in this chapter.

B. *Results from Observations of Sound Waves*

The way in which the sound of a large explosion is heard at places around it presents an abnormality that had been known for a long time, but had never been explained satisfactorily. In the immediate neighbourhood of the explosion the sound is naturally heard on all sides, but frequently, at distances of less than 80 km the sound ceases to be heard. However, the sound is often strongly heard again at distances of, say, 200 to 300 km. The sound which is heard at these great distances has clearly not come through the air near the ground, otherwise it would have been heard at the intermediate places. Further, it is found that the sound has taken some 2 minutes longer to reach the 'outer zone' than if it had come directly. For these reasons it was thought that the sound waves had passed up into the upper air and had been bent down to earth again. The problem was to know why the sound waves had been bent down in the upper atmosphere, instead of continuing to travel upwards. As soon as the upper warm region was discovered, the reason for the downward bending of the sound waves became clear.

Sound travels faster through warm air than through cold air, the velocity being, in fact, proportional to the square root of the temperature when measured on the absolute scale. If sound waves travel through a region where the temperature is changing with height, the waves will be bent towards the colder part. Thus the sound waves travelling outwards along the ground, near the explosion, will be bent upwards on account of the general fall of temperature with height near the ground. This, in addition to the absorption of the sound by obstacles on the ground, accounts for the fact that the sound is heard in the area around the explosion to limited distances only. Some of the sound waves will pass upwards into the stratosphere and eventually come to the lower part of the warm region at a height of some 50 km where the temperature is rising rapidly with height. Here they will again be bent towards the colder part, i.e. they will be bent downwards and, after passing down through the stratosphere and troposphere, will be heard at the 'abnormal' distances of 200 to 300 km.

Fig. 3.2 shows on the left a general indication of the way the temperature changes with height, and on the right some of the

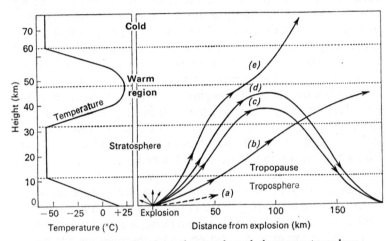

FIG. 3.2. Possible paths of sound waves through the upper atmosphere.

The curve on the left indicates the average temperature at different heights. Curves (a) to (d) show how sound waves are refracted upwards in the troposphere where the temperature falls with height, and downwards in the lower part of the warm region where the temperature rises with height. Curve (e) starts out at too steep an angle to be refracted back to earth.

possible paths of sound waves from an explosion. Ray (a) travelling out along the ground is soon absorbed; ray (b) starting out at a small angle upwards will be bent still more upwards and may eventually reach the ground again but at a very great distance; rays (c) and (d) are bent upwards in the troposphere and, on entering the region where the temperature increases with height they are bent down again, to reach the ground at some place 200 to 300 km away. It will be noticed that it is possible for sound to reach a place in the outer zone by two different paths, such as (c) and (d) having different lengths and having travelled to different heights in the atmosphere. In such cases a single explosion will be heard as two separate bangs, separated by a short interval of time. If a sound ray such as (e) starts out at too steep an angle it may not be bent enough to return to the ground.

The bending of the sound ray on striking the warm layer of air is similar to the bending of light on passing from air into glass. It may also be compared to the turning round of long waves at sea coming in to a shelving coast. It must often have been noticed that, though the waves out at sea may be coming in at an angle to the shore, yet by the time they break they have turned round so that the wave-crests lie nearly parallel to the shore. The speed of such sea waves depends on the depth of the water through which they are passing, being greater in deep water than in shallow water. Thus the part of the wave which approaches the shore first begins to slow down, while another part, further along the wave, and still in deep water, will continue to travel fast, with the result that the wave-crest gradually swings round and finally becomes nearly parallel to the shore. Fig. 3.3 illustrates in greater detail the bending of a sound wave when different parts of its wave-front travel at different speeds.

Once these general facts were known, steps were taken to measure the temperature in the upper warm region by observing sound waves. Little can be got from large, accidental explosions since, not being expected, no accurate observations are made. Fortunately quite small explosions can be recorded by suitable microphones placed in the outer zone, so that small explosions, specially made for the purpose, can be used, or even the normal firing of large guns in practice. In some cases aircraft have been used to drop a series of bombs over the sea in suitable lines radiating out from a central station fitted with microphones, when the effect of wind—which in other cases is a disturbing factor—can be allowed for.

It is possible to measure both the total time that the sound waves have taken on their journey and also the angle at which the sound ray comes down to the ground at the end of its path. This angle is measured by placing three or more microphones, suitably arranged, at a distance of a few hundred metres apart in the outer zone. The temperature and wind in the lowest 20 to 30 km of air are also measured at the same time by balloons, so that the various possible paths of the sound waves through this part of the atmosphere can be calculated. It is then a matter of trial to find a possible path which will fit both the total time of travel and the angle at which the sound ray comes down to ground. In practice, the uncertainty is not great, and both the highest point reached by the ray and its velocity at this height

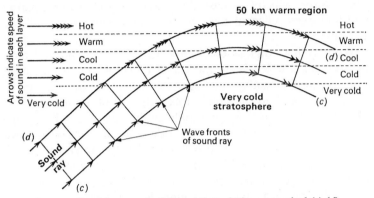

FIG. 3.3. An enlargement of the portion of Fig. 3.2 marked (c) (d).

The arrows on the left show (much exaggerated) the distance travelled by sound in a given time at different heights, in a region where the temperature rises with height. The solid cross-lines show successive positions of a wave-front after equal intervals of time. The distance moved by the wave-front in the given interval of time is equal to the length of the arrow at the appropriate height. It is seen that the wavefront is gradually turned round, with the consequence that the direction of propagation of the sound is gradually bent downwards.

can be found, from which the temperature is obtained. If more than one bang is heard at the receiving station, this gives no trouble, but rather is an advantage since the temperature at another height can be calculated.

The temperature of the upper atmosphere has been explored by this method in many widely different parts of the world and in all cases a warm region was present. As in the case of the lower stratosphere, the highest temperature in this 50 km warm region is found in polar latitudes in the summer. Even in the polar winter, when the lower stratosphere is very cold, the upper warm region is still present, though probably not so warm as in the summer. As mentioned in Chapter 1, the warm region is caused by the absorption of ultra-violet sunlight by ozone, but this will be fully discussed at the end of this chapter.

Unfortunately this method cannot be used to explore the air above the height where the temperature is a maximum, since sound waves such as (e) in Fig. 3.2 are bent upwards in the higher part of the warm region and do not return to earth. Observations made at the time of the great explosion at Heligoland just after the Second World War, gave some indication of sound waves which had passed through the 50 km warm region and had been reflected back by the still warmer region above 100 km.

We may here digress to discuss the effect of wind and temperature at low levels on the travel of sound in producing a local phenomenon that most people will have noticed but of which few may know the real explanation. Suppose some source of noise, a noisy factory or a railway line, exists a mile or two away, say to the east. On most days the noise will not be noticed, but occasionally it will be heard very clearly and someone will generally remark that 'The wind must have gone into the east because the trains are heard so clearly'. True, the wind will, probably, be east, but the sound is not heard to unusual distances because it is 'carried by the wind'. This is fairly obvious when one remembers that, while a moderate wind may have a speed of some 20 km/h, the speed of sound is more nearly 20 km/min; such a small increase of the speed of the sound due to the wind would make a negligible difference to the distance to which it could be heard. The real explanation why sound tends to be heard more easily down-wind than up-wind is this: the speed of the wind near the ground level is normally very much less than that some 200 or 300 m up, and there is generally a steady increase of wind speed with height. Those sound waves which start to travel outwards along the ground are soon damped out, while those that start out at a small angle upwards generally continue upwards and indeed, as we have already seen, will tend to be bent still more upwards by the normal decrease of temperature with height in the troposphere. For this reason the sound is generally heard to no great distance. However, if the wind speed increases rather rapidly with height, the total velocity of the sound wave travelling down-wind (i.e. normal sound velocity plus wind) may be greater at, say, 300 m than at 100 m, in which case the sound wave will be bent back to earth. These sound waves suffer no absorption due to obstacles on the ground, so that if they do come down to ground again they will be strongly heard several kilometres from their source. It is therefore the *increase* of wind speed with height which causes the sound to be heard better down-wind. A similar effect would be produced if (as hardly ever happens) the wind were very strong at ground level and *decreased* in speed with height, except that then the sound would be better heard *up-wind*.

The effect of air temperature on local sources of sound may also often be noticed, and this is produced in exactly the same way as that by the warm region at a height of 50 km except that the increase of temperature is only some few hundred metres up. On a calm, clear night the air near the ground cools quickly while that higher up remains warm (as may be noticed when going up and down a hill at such times). During the course of the night the cold layer may extend up to 100 m or so, while above this there is a sharp increase of temperature. This increase of temperature will cause the sound waves which pass up to it to be bent downwards so that sources of noise which are not normally noticed may be heard quite loudly a mile or two away. A light wind, which is not strong enough to destroy the pool of cold air near the ground, will add to the effect if it is blowing in the right direction.

c. *Observations using Rockets*

Rocket-borne apparatus has been of great use in measuring the temperature of the upper air. The information is usually transmitted to the ground by radio, as in the case of radiosondes. It is not possible to measure the temperature of the air directly by thermometers carried on the rocket, because of the very high speed of the rocket through the air. Just as a meteor is heated in passing through the air, so the skin of the rocket and any instruments exposed to the air stream are also heated far above the temperature of the surrounding air, so that indirect methods have to be used. Pressure or density gauges can be carried on the rocket which, after correcting for the rocket's speed, do give the true pressure or density of the surrounding air.

Very valuable measurements of the temperature and winds up to a height of 50 to 70 km are now being made by an organization known as the Meteorological Rocket Network which has some fifty stations in North America, parts of the Pacific and Atlantic Oceans, and one station in the Hebrides. The instruments are carried up on small rockets and released at the maximum height, after which they fall slowly on a parachute and the results are transmitted to the ground by radio.

Because the density of the air is very low at these heights, it is difficult to measure its temperature accurately. This is because the conduction of heat between the air and the thermometer becomes very small. Heating or cooling of the thermometer by radiation may make its temperature appreciably different from that of the surrounding air. Again the conduction of heat along the supports of the thermometer and its electrical connections must be made very small. In practice very small thermistors are used. These are small beads of a semiconductor whose electrical resistance changes very rapidly with change of temperature. The beads are only about 1/100 in in diameter and are coated with a reflecting surface to minimize effects of radiation. The thermistors are mounted on very thin mylar film to reduce the conduction of heat and they give a reasonably accurate measurement of the air temperature up to heights of 50 km or more.

Rocket-borne grenades

We have already seen how the temperature of the upper air can be measured by using the observations of sound waves which have travelled up into the upper air and back again. Such measurements can only be made up to a height of about 50 km. Greater heights can be obtained and more direct measurements can be made if grenades, containing a few pounds of high explosive, are carried up on a rocket and are ejected and fired at suitable intervals as the rocket ascends, between heights of about 30 and 100 km. The position of each explosion may be found by photographing the flash (at night) by cameras suitably spaced on the ground, while the time taken for the sound to travel down to ground level is measured by microphones. Alternatively, the rocket may be tracked very accurately by radio methods and the moment of firing each grenade signalled down by radio. Using this method, measurements can be made when the sky is cloudy, and by day as well as by night. The velocity of sound within each interval of height is found, and from this the temperature of the air at that level is obtained.

The sound of the explosions becomes too weak to be recorded if they are made above about 120 km. Another method which involves the velocity of sound is to measure the angle of the bow-wave from the rocket and, since this depends both on the rocket's speed and the velocity of sound in the surrounding air, it is possible to measure the temperature of the air at different heights.

Resistance of falling spheres

A method which has proved very successful uses the fact that the resistance experienced by a sphere, falling freely through the air, depends on the density of the air through which it falls. If the density is low, then the sphere will fall fast, while if the density is high it will fall slowly. The sphere is carried folded in the rocket, and ejected at the desired height and immediately inflated. The sphere contains a small radio transmitter and its height and speed of fall are measured by radio methods from the ground. Thus the air resistance experienced by the falling sphere is obtained, and from this the density of the air can be calculated at all heights. Again the temperature of the air is calculated from the change of density with height.

An interesting variation of this method is to measure the resistance of a body falling freely through the air in the following way. A hollow metal ball is ejected from the ascending rocket in the upper part of its flight; thereafter the ball will continue its flight upwards for some time and then fall back to earth. At the centre of the ball is a small hollow sphere, and at the centre of this again is a small body which can be released when required. Let us suppose first, that the whole apparatus has been released far out in space, where there is no appreciable amount of air to resist its motion; in this case it will move freely, being influenced only by gravity. If the small central body is now released, both it and the rest of the apparatus will be subject to no forces other than the earth's gravity, so that although the small central body is not now connected to the rest of the apparatus, it will continue to move with the main sphere and will remain at the centre of that sphere. Now let us suppose that the apparatus falls into the atmosphere where there is some resistance from the air. The main outer ball will be slowed up by this resistance, while the inner, central body continues to move under the force of gravity only, and it will catch up the other parts of the apparatus and hit its container. The more quickly the apparatus is slowed down by the resistance of the air, the faster will the inner body catch it up and the quicker will it hit its container. The time between its release and its hitting the container is thus a measure of the air resistance to the outer sphere. Arrangements are made to return the small body to the centre of its sphere and release it again and again. The apparatus has a radio transmitter which sends out signals when the small central body is released and also when it hits its container. From the time between these two signals, the resistance to the apparatus by the air is found. If the apparatus is tracked by radio methods, its height and velocity at any time are known, and, since the resistance to the sphere depends on its speed and the density of the surrounding air, it is easy to calculate this density. As before, the temperature at any height is calculated from the rate of change of density at that height. The results can be checked at the lower levels by comparison with the density measured by instruments on balloons. The method can be used up to heights of about 90 km and the variations of temperature in the warm region at 50 km can be accurately measured.

D. *Searchlights*

If a searchlight is pointed upwards on a dark night, the beam is visible up to a considerable height, chiefly owing to scattering by dust and haze particles in the air, but also owing to scattering by the air itself. In the upper atmosphere there will probably be little dust or haze and if the scattering is due to air alone, the amount of scattering will be a measure of the density of the air. Since the background of skylight, even on a dark night, would spoil the results, the searchlight is made to emit a regularly fluctuating light and only the fluctuations are measured, so that skylight is eliminated. In practice, a searchlight is fixed pointing upwards and some 20 or 30 km away another searchlight mirror is set up, but, instead of containing a source of light, a sensitive photocell (usually a photomultiplier) is fixed at the focus of the mirror, so that the photocell collects light from a volume of air just like that in the beam of the searchlight. The two 'searchlights' are arranged so that their 'beams' cross, and one or other is rocked backwards and forwards so that the point of crossing moves up and down in the atmosphere while the intensity of the scattered light is measured. The method has been used to measure densities up to about 70 km, but of course, it can only be used in a very clear, cloudless sky and, preferably, from a high-level station.

An alternative method is to use a pulsed source of light in which light is emitted in very intense, but very short, pulses. The height at which the light is scattered back is measured by the lapse of time between the emission of the pulse and the reception of the scattered light. The intensity of the scattered pulse depends on the amount of scattering material (air and dust) at the particular height. It has recently been shown that there is more dust in the stratosphere than was expected, so that these methods are of more use in detecting these dusty layers than in measuring the density of the air. This is particularly the case now that small, and relatively cheap, rockets are available to carry small instruments up to these heights. Much of the dust in the stratosphere is believed to be produced by the evaporation and condensation of meteors. (See p. 43)

Temperature of the air between 30 and 100 km. All the measurements of temperature, by whatever method they have been made, at all times of the year and in all latitudes, have always shown the existence of a warm region at a height of 50 km, so that it seems that this is a general characteristic of the atmosphere.

While many more measurements are necessary before we know the details of the variations of temperature at these levels with season and with latitude (and possibly with solar activity) Fig. 3.4 gives a general indication of the vertical distribution of temperature in high and low latitudes. It is emphasized that this diagram should not be taken as more than a general indication of the temperatures. The very low temperatures shown at a height of about 80 to 85 km at all seasons in low latitudes, and in summer in high latitudes, is almost certainly correct. Perhaps the most remarkable thing is the relatively high temperature found around 80 km in the polar winter, but it seems that this also is correct.

Noctilucent clouds. Occasionally very thin clouds are visible long after sunset and when in 1885 calculations were first made of the height at which such clouds must be, in order that they may be still lit up by the sun, it was found that they were at the extraordinary height of about 80 km. Clearly they were no ordinary clouds. Being visible only in the dark sky after sunset, they were called noctilucent clouds.

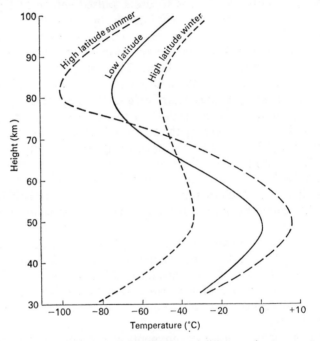

FIG. 3.4. This diagram indicates the general differences in temperature between the equator, the summer pole, and the winter pole at different heights between 30 and 100 km. Details may well be changed by further measurements. Note the unexpected differences of temperature at heights around 80 to 90 km.

The very low temperature of the air at a height of about 80 km in summer in high latitudes seems to be connected with the formation of these clouds; indeed the existence of clouds at this level first led to the suggestion that there was a very cold region here, before any actual measurement of the temperature at these heights was possible. Noctilucent clouds are rather similar in appearance to mother-of-pearl clouds, but are much higher and more tenuous. Unlike the mother-of-pearl clouds, they show no colour but appear silvery white. The height of many of these clouds has been measured by taking simultaneous photographs from two distant places and they are always found to be between about 75 and 90 km, while they are most frequently close to 85 km, i.e. just about the height of the minimum temperature shown in Fig. 3.4. They are most frequently visible in latitudes between 55 and 65°. Although they have been observed much more frequently in the northern hemisphere than in the southern hemisphere, this is probably because there are many more people to watch for them. Their occurrence is limited to the summer months and they are seen most frequently just after midsummer. Since a regular watch has been kept for these clouds at many places, it has been found that they are more common than was previously thought and it has been estimated that during the month of July, when they are most common, they can generally be seen from somewhere in the northern hemisphere on each night.

Very little is known for certain about their physical condition or how they are formed. It is not even certain whether they are ice particles or dust. When rockets were sent up in Scandinavia to collect samples of dust and to measure the temperature at the height of the clouds, it was found that when the clouds were visible the temperature was abnormally low and very much more dust was present than when there were no clouds. The dust particles were very small—less than the wavelength of light—and there was some evidence that, when they were collected, they were coated with ice, though, of course, this evaporated before they could be examined. The dust seemed to be composed largely of iron or nickel, which makes it probably that it was of meteoric origin. After the great Siberian meteorite of 30 June 1908 similar but very much brighter clouds were seen over a wide area in northern latitudes. This would add weight to the suggestion that meteoric dust was involved. As will be seen from Fig. 3.4 the temperature of the air falls rapidly with increasing height in the region below 80 km just as it does in the troposphere, so that there may well be much mixing of the air here and any meteoric dust which fell below this level would be rapidly dispersed downwards. Above 85 km the air will be much more stable, with little mixing so that meteoric dust would fall slowly and a dusty layer might be formed around 85 km.

Calculation of the temperature from the pressure or density. Fig. 3.5 is given to illustrate the way in which the variation of density with height depends on the temperature of the air. The curve on the right shows an idealized distribution of temperature with height in the atmosphere, while the curve on the left shows the decrease of density with height under these conditions. It will be noted that in the three regions with constant temperature, the density curve is a straight line (when the density is plotted

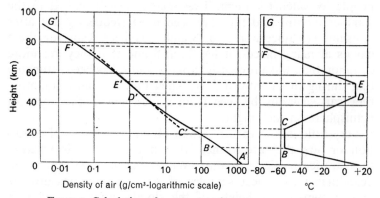

FIG. 3.5. Calculation of temperature from pressure or density.

The diagram indicates the way in which the change of temperature with height may be calculated from the change of density with height. An idealized temperature distribution is shown on the right while the change of density with height is shown on the left, the density scale being logarithmic. Note that the density falls quickly with height when the temperature is low, but slowly when the temperature is high.

on a logarithmic scale) and that the slope depends on the temperature; thus in the region *DE*, where the temperature is high, the decrease in density is slower than in the cold regions *BC* and *FG*. If we can obtain the distribution of density with height from rockets, searchlights, or meteor observations, we can calculate the temperature distribution. If we had plotted pressure instead of density, the diagram would have been very similar, and the temperature could have been obtained in the same way.

2. TEMPERATURE AT GREAT HEIGHTS (ABOVE 100 KM)

A. *Use of Artificial Satellites*

At heights above 100 km it is much more difficult to measure the temperature of the air. Rockets can, of course, go to any height, but the most accurate methods of measuring temperature with the aid of rockets cannot be used here. Measurements of the velocity of sound from grenades cannot be made because, owing to the very low density of the air, the sound is too faint to be recorded at ground level. Again the drag on a falling sphere is too small to be measured accurately. A method which is giving useful results even at very great heights is the measurement of the atmospheric drag on artificial earth satellites. The speed of a satellite is very high so that the drag, which depends on the density of the air, may be appreciable although the density of the air is very low, and it can be found from the change in the path of the satellite as it continually circles the earth. The speed and path of the satellite can be measured very accurately, so that although the resistance of the air is very small owing to its low density, yet this resistance, and hence the density of the air, can be calculated accurately. This particularly applies to the large, light spheres such as Early Bird which are used for radio communications. Most satellites do not move round the earth at a constant height, and the effect of the resistance of the air is greatest at those times when they come lowest into the atmosphere. The effect of the resistance of the air is to reduce their maximum height and to make them circle the earth faster, the minimum height remaining nearly constant.

Satellites have an advantage over rockets for the measurement of the density of the upper air, because they remain in their orbits for many months or years, and since their minimum height above the earth changes little during this time, a long series of measurements of the density of the air at this minimum height can be obtained. As a result of these measurements we now know that the atmosphere extends to an even greater altitude than was previously thought. In addition, it has been found that the density of the air at very great heights varies by remarkably large amounts. These changes in density are largely due to changes in the temperature of the air, but it has to be remembered that at these great altitudes the air no longer consists primarily of oxygen and nitrogen molecules, but that many molecules (particularly oxygen molecules) are dissociated into oxygen atoms. Changes in the density of the air will be caused by changes in the amount of dissociation as well as by changes of temperature so that unless we know the composition of the air at these great heights, we cannot deduce the temperature with certainty.

At heights above 200 to 300 km there are fundamental differences compared with lower levels.

(a) Mixing by turbulent (eddy) diffusion is so small here that the light and heavy gases are no longer mixed together in a constant proportion, but the density of each gas falls off with height at a rate which depends only on the temperature and molecular weight of the gas, and is independent of the presence of other lighter or heavier gases. Thus a heavy gas, such as molecular nitrogen, falls off comparatively rapidly with increasing height, while lighter gases, e.g. atomic oxygen, helium, and hydrogen, fall off more slowly. It is for this reason that, while molecular nitrogen is much the most abundant gas at low levels, it is surpassed by atomic oxygen at heights above about 200 to 300 km, while at still higher levels helium may be predominant and this is finally surpassed, at perhaps 2000 km, by atomic hydrogen. These heights, however, vary greatly according to the season, the sun-spot cycle, etc.

(b) In the troposphere the transfer of heat from one region to another is mainly by eddy diffusion. In the stratosphere, where turbulence is very much smaller, the transference of heat by radiation is more important. In both these lower regions of the atmosphere molecular conduction of heat (i.e. that due to the motion of individual molecules) is relatively unimportant. However, at the very high levels with which we are now dealing, the turbulence is small, while the density of the air is so low that the emission and absorption of long-wave radiation are small. On the other hand, the molecular conduction of heat is not reduced at low densities because the decrease in the number of molecules is balanced by their longer mean free path. (Since there are no 'walls' in the atmosphere, the mean free path of a molecule can increase indefinitely, in contrast to the case of an evacuated vessel—e.g. a vacuum flask—where the mean free path is limited by the walls and as soon as the mean free path becomes greater than the distance between the walls, the molecular conductivity *is* reduced, owing to the reduction in the number of molecules.) Since the heat capacity of the very rare air at great heights is exceedingly small, only very small amounts of heat will change its temperature greatly and local differences of temperature are quickly smoothed out by molecular conduction. For this reason the temperature of the air above 200 to 300 km shows little change with height and we have a nearly isothermal region.

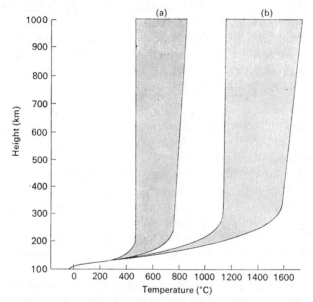

FIG. 3.6. Temperature in the thermosphere. The shaded area indicates the daily range of temperature at different heights, (a) for days around sun-spot minimum and (b) for days around sun-spot maximum. The temperature varies so greatly from day to day with solar activity that mean curves would have little meaning.

The temperature of the air rises rapidly above a height of 85 km where it is usually very low (except during the polar winter) until the very hot, isothermal region—the thermosphere—is reached. While the temperature of the thermosphere is roughly constant at all heights at any given time and place, the region undergoes large changes of temperature from one time to another, varying from about 400 to over 2000° C. These variations of temperature may be divided into various classes as follows:

(a) A diurnal variation of temperature with a maximum about 2 hours after noon and a minimum near sunrise. Range about 500 to 800° C.

(b) An annual (not seasonal) variation with a maximum in January and a minimum in July. Range 100 to 200° C.

(c) A semi-annual variation with maxima in April and October and minima in January and July. Range 200 to 300° C.

(d) An 11-year cycle with maximun probably at the sun-spot maximum and minimum at sun-spot minimum.

(e) Variations from day to day which are connected with the solar activity as indicated by magnetic storms, solar flares, and increase in solar radio waves (see Chapter 7).

(f) Changes with latitude.

It will be understood that a long series of measurements will be necessary before these different types of variation of temperature can be separated out from one another. Thus the range of the diurnal variation apparently depends on the part of the 11-year solar cycle at which the measurements are made. The first artificial earth satellites were sent up at a time of unusually high sun-spot activity and at the present time we have only just passed the following sun-spot minimum. When measurements have been continued for two or three complete 11-year sun-spot periods it may well be found that the above account requires some modification.

It seems that much of the variation of temperature at very great heights is caused by variations in solar ultra-violet radiation, but corpuscular radiation from the sun probably also has an effect.

3. WHY HAS THE TEMPERATURE OF THE ATMOSPHERE THIS PECULIAR DISTRIBUTION?

A. *Note on Radiation*

In order to understand the following discussion it is essential that the reader should have a clear idea of the different types of radiation with which we shall have to deal, and the following brief note may be useful to those who are not familiar with the subject.

Light is an electromagnetic wave radiation, as also are radio waves, infra-red 'heat' radiation, ultra-violet radiation, X-rays, and the 'gamma' rays from radioactive substances. These are therefore all of the same nature and they differ from one another only in wavelength, i.e. they differ in the same way as two musical notes differ. Table 3.1 has been drawn up to try to convey an idea of the actual wavelengths involved, and it will be seen that they range from the microscopically small, right up

TABLE 3.1. *Wavelengths*

Electromagnetic radiation

Radio waves

Very long	Several kilometres	Several miles
Medium broadcasting	Few hundred metres	Several hundred feet
Short-wave broadcasting	Few metres	Several feet
Very short waves	Few millimetres	Fractions of an inch

Infra-red radiant heat

	$\left\{\begin{array}{l} 0\cdot1 \text{ to } 0\cdot001 \text{ mm} \\ 1\,000\,000 \text{ to } 10\,000 \text{ Å} \\ 100\ \mu\text{m to } 1\ \mu\text{m} \end{array}\right\}$	$1/250$ to $1/25\,000$ in

Visible light

Extreme Red	$0\cdot0008$ mm $\equiv 8000$ Å	$0\cdot000003$ in
Extreme Violet	$0\cdot0004$ mm $\equiv 4000$ Å	$0\cdot000001$ in
Ultra-violet	4000 to 500 Å	
X-rays	500 to $0\cdot1$ Å	
Gamma rays	$0\cdot1$ to $0\cdot00001$ Å	

Sound waves

Lowest audible note	approx. 20 m	60 ft
Lowest note on piano	approx. 10 m	30 ft
Highest note on piano	approx. 10 cm	4 in
Highest audible note	approx. 1 cm	$\frac{1}{2}$ in

Note: One angstrom unit (Å) $= 1/10\,000\,000$ mm. One micron (μm) $= 1/1000$ mm.

to several kilometres. The wavelengths of some sound waves have been added for comparison. In the case of both sound and light, the ear or the eye can detect only a small part of the whole range of wavelengths which exists.

Although the whole range of electromagnetic radiation from radio waves, through light, to gamma rays is essentially of the same nature, yet the usual methods by which the different types of radiation are produced and detected differ greatly and the different types of radiation have very different properties. However, radiation from a very hot solid includes all types of radiation, though the very long and the very short wavelengths are emitted in quite negligible amounts, most of the energy being in the intermediate wavelengths. While, in principle, all types of radiation can be detected by measuring the heating which they cause when they are absorbed, in most cases more convenient and more sensitive methods are possible, e.g. the radio receiver for radio waves, the photocell or the photographic plate for visible and ultra-violet radiation.

While any hot solid emits radiation over a large range of wavelengths, the region of the spectrum at which most of the energy is emitted varies greatly with the temperature of the hot body, as can be seen from the following illustrations. The radiation from a poker, heated to bright redness in a fire, can be seen as well as felt. As the poker cools, the visible light becomes fainter and redder, until finally the poker is no longer visible even in the dark, but the infra-red radiant heat which it emits can still easily be felt.

To take another example, a small bright electric bulb and a large black kettle at boiling point may each radiate away the same amount of heat, but it is clear that their radiations are of very different character; much of the radiation from the electric bulb is in the visible part of the spectrum or in the 'near' infra-red region with wavelengths shorter than about 3 μm. In the case of the kettle none of the radiation is visible, but is all in the long-wave region in the 'far' infra-red (say 5 to 30 μm). We shall be considering the radiation emitted by the sun and by the earth and, since the sun is much hotter than an electric filament and the earth is cooler than a boiling kettle, their radiations will be even more different than those of the electric bulb and the kettle.

We must also note that radiations of different wavelengths may have very different properties; thus ordinary glass is transparent to visible light but is opaque to much of the ultra-violet radiation; both radio waves and X-rays (though at the opposite ends of the spectrum) can penetrate many substances which are opaque to visible light; water vapour is transparent to visible light but is very opaque to much of the infra-red radiation. These different properties are of great importance in the physics of the atmosphere. We shall now return to the consideration of the temperature of the air.

B. *General Principles*

It must be stated at the outset that our knowledge of the way in which the temperature of the air at the various levels is controlled is far from complete. While the broad outlines are thought to be well established, there are many points which are still not clear. A quarter of a century ago we thought that we understood the question fairly well, but more recent observations have raised difficulties which are not yet solved. It has been well said that it is easy to be certain when you know very little! He would be a bold person who supposed that the views which we now hold would still be thought adequate a quarter of a century ahead. Further, the account of the thermal processes in the atmosphere which is given below is greatly oversimplified. If we tried to set out in detail, even what is thought to be known at the present time, it would be necessary to devote most of this book to the subject!

It is first necessary to set out four general principles which are fundamental to the discussion that follows.

The temperature of the atmosphere and of the surface of the earth is entirely governed by the radiant heat received from the sun. The supply of the earth's internal heat to the surface is negligible. If the radiation from the sun were cut off, the ground and the atmosphere would cool down to a very low temperature.

Since, over a long period of time, the earth is not becoming appreciably warmer, all the heat from the sun which is absorbed by the ground and the atmosphere must eventually be re-radiated back into space.

The temperature of the sun is of the order of 6000° C while the average temperature of the earth is about 10° C. Fig. 3.7 gives the relative amounts of energy in the different wavelengths as radiated by two bodies, one at 6000° C and the other at 10° C. The solar energy is nearly all in the visible part of the spectrum while that from the earth, like the kettle, is entirely invisible in the 'far' infra-red region (say 5 to 30 μm).

Below the curve of Fig. 3.7 three diagrams are added which refer to three levels in the atmosphere and indicate the regions of the spectrum where there is strong absorption by water vapour, carbon dioxide, and ozone. These three diagrams refer

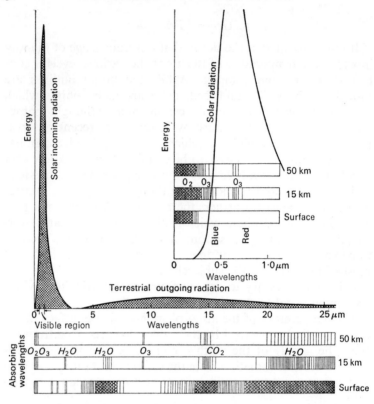

FIG. 3.7. Spectral distribution of solar and terrestrial radiation.

The curves marked solar and terrestrial radiation indicate the distribution of energy in the different wavelengths of radiation from these two
sources. Note that the energy of the incoming solar, and the outgoing
terrestrial radiation lie in quite separate parts of the spectrum. (Blue light
has a wavelength of about 0·4 μm and a red light about 0·7 μm.) The shaded
strips below the curves indicate the wavelengths where the atmosphere absorbs
radiation. Note that there is much absorption of the outgoing terrestrial radiation by the lower layers but little by the highest layers.

The small inset shows the short-wavelength end of the diagram with a
more open wavelength scale.

to the surface layers, to the lower stratosphere, say about 15 km,
and to the warm region at a height of about 50 km. The important thing to notice in this figure is that the incoming solar
radiation suffers only relatively small absorption by the atmosphere (and this absorption is in the ultra-violet wavelengths)
but the out-going, terrestrial radiation suffers much absorption

by the lower atmosphere, particularly in the infra-red part of the spectrum chiefly near 6 μm and beyond 15 μm.

While by far the greater part of the energy radiated by the sun (in the visible, the 'near' ultra-violet, and the infra-red regions) comes from the photosphere—the visible disc of the sun—the corona also gives rise to much weaker, but very important, radiation in the 'far' ultra-violet and X-ray regions. These radiations are strongly absorbed high in the atmosphere. The corona also gives rise to radio waves, but these have little effect on the atmosphere although they form a very useful measure of the activity of the sun. Quite apart from the above wave radiations, the sun emits streams of electrically charged particles. These are also absorbed high in the atmosphere and in certain conditions probably have some effect in heating the air.

We shall now follow the sun's radiation from the time it first enters the highest part of the atmosphere until it is finally re-radiated away again into space. In doing so we shall see how it comes about that there are three warm regions in the atmosphere separated by two cold regions.

The upper part of the thermosphere is so very rare that little solar radiation of any kind is absorbed here, but the high effective thermal conductivity causes its temperature to follow that of the lower regions (say 300 km) where the density is high enough to absorb solar radiation.

The shortest ultra-violet wavelengths of sunlight (shorter than about 1800 Å) are so strongly absorbed by molecular oxygen that the small amount of molecular oxygen above 100 km height absorbs all the energy that there is in this part of the solar spectrum before it has travelled down to this level. The extremely short, X-ray, wavelengths in sunlight are also absorbed at great heights; this is important for the formation of the ionosphere which we shall discuss in a later chapter. The absorption of this ultra-violet solar radiation will warm the air until it is hot enough to get rid of heat as fast as it receives it. This is one cause of the very high temperature of the layers above 200 km.

We have seen that the temperature of the thermosphere varies not only with the season and the time of day, but also with the 11-year sun-spot period and it is warmed at times of solar flares and magnetic storms. It also has the curious 6-month period with maxima in spring and autumn and minima in summer and winter. As will be seen later, the frequency of the occurrence of large magnetic storms and of auroras also shows this peculiar 6-month period. This suggests that there are two sources of solar heating, viz. (1) very short-wave ultra-violet radiation and (2) corpuscular radiation. The changes in the temperature of the thermosphere are greater in very high latitudes than in low latitudes, which again suggests that some of the warming is caused by electrically charged particles, since these charged particles will be deflected to the polar regions while the wave radiation will fall uniformly on the illuminated side of the earth.

The annual variation of temperature in the thermosphere (maximum in January and minimum in July) is also somewhat of a mystery since, although the earth is about 6 per cent nearer to the sun in January than in July, this does not seem enough to cause the observed amount of warming. Sudden variations of temperature at the times of solar flares and magnetic storms might be caused by either wave radiation or corpuscular radiation, but in the latter case there would presumably be a lag of about a day or two between the solar flare and the warming. It has been suggested that such a time lag is indeed present. However, we must remember that the exact amounts of these warmings and the times of maxima and minima are still not well known.

As the solar radiation travels on downwards, depleted only of its extreme ultra-violet wavelengths shorter than about 1800 Å, it will suffer little further absorption for some distance, and it is presumably for this reason that the air is cold at a height of about 85 km—the height of the noctilucent clouds. At still lower levels where the density of the air is greater, ultra-violet light of wavelengths between about 2000 and 2400 Å will be absorbed by molecular oxygen. This absorption causes an oxygen molecule to be dissociated into two oxygen atoms and the reaction between oxygen atoms and oxygen molecules forms ozone.

When the solar radiation reaches a level of about 60 km above the ground, it will begin to encounter the upper part of the ozone-rich region and, though the amount of ozone at such heights is very small, yet so strong is its absorption of ultra-violet radiation, that a large part of the solar energy in the wavelengths between 2000 and 3000 Å is absorbed. In all, some 5 per cent of the incoming solar radiation is absorbed, mainly above 40 km. This energy will warm the air until the heat lost by radiation (in the very long wavelengths) is equal to that absorbed which happens when the temperature has risen to about that of the earth's surface. In this way the middle warm region is formed at a height of about 50 km.

The reason why the air at a height of about 80 km in polar regions is warmer in winter than in summer is still not well understood. It is presumably due to subsidence of the air causing dynamic warming, but it has been suggested that if air containing much atomic oxygen sinks to lower levels the oxygen atoms will combine to oxygen molecules and enough heat may be released in this process to warm the air.

Solar radiation, now depleted of much of its ultra-violet wave-lengths in the two upper warm regions, is subject to little further absorption on its journey all the way down to the earth's surface. There will, indeed, be some further absorption of ultra-violet sunlight by ozone in the stratosphere (and a little by a weak ozone band in the visible region) which will cause the stratosphere to be warmer than it otherwise would be, but the details of this have not yet been fully studied.

About half of the incoming sunlight is reflected back by clouds and by the surface of the earth. This energy, being *reflected* and not *absorbed*, causes no warming of the clouds or of the ground. The other half of the sunlight which is absorbed by the ground and the air is of the greatest importance, since it provides the whole of the heat necessary to keep the earth and the atmosphere warm, and also supplies the energy of winds, rain, and all other atmospheric activities.

With its final absorption by the earth's surface, the history of the solar radiation as such comes to an end, but the earth's surface must get rid of as much heat as it absorbs, and it does this partly by radiation and partly by the evaporation of water, which goes into the air as water vapour, where, when it condenses again, it gives to the air as much heat as was required to evaporate it. We have already seen that since the average temperature of the ground is about 10° C, the radiation from it will be in the 'far' infra-red region where water vapour and carbon dioxide strongly absorb radiation—water vapour being particularly important at very low levels (see Fig. 3.7). As a result, the terrestrial radiation does not travel far upwards before most of it is absorbed, only to be re-radiated again, but now half will be radiated upwards and the other half back to the ground where it is again absorbed. The half of the radiation which was emitted upwards is again quickly absorbed by water vapour only a little higher up, again to be re-radiated, half upwards and half downwards, some of the latter reaching the ground. As a result of this complicated process of constant absorption and re-emission of radiation, it comes about that the ground not only absorbs about half of the incoming solar radiation, but it also has returned to it much of the very long wave radiation which it, itself, has just radiated. The effect of water vapour and carbon dioxide in the lowest atmosphere in absorbing and re-radiating heat radiated by the ground may be likened to the effect of fog on a beam of light from a searchlight, pointing upwards on a dark night. The light is quickly intercepted by the fog and scattered in all directions, with the result that much of the light is finally returned to the ground which is illuminated much more brightly than it would have been in the absence of the fog. This action of water vapour and carbon dioxide in the lower air is often known as the glass-house effect, since glass, like water vapour and carbon dioxide, allows the incoming, visible radiation from the sun to pass freely through it, but is opaque to the long-wave, infra-red radiation. The outgoing radiation from within the glass-house thus finds it difficult to pass through the glass, and even if the glass is warmed by it, much of the heat is radiated back to the inside of the glass-house, so that the temperature of the glass-house is raised above that outside.

The fact that the intensity of the outgoing radiation, as it passes through the lower atmosphere, falls off rapidly with height—just as the light from a searchlight on a foggy night falls off rapidly—would lead to a very rapid fall of air temperature with height if radiation were the controlling factor. Such a rapid fall of temperature would cause the air at higher levels to be heavier than that at lower levels, and rapid vertical mixing of the air would ensue, which would give rise to a much slower fall of temperature with height. The actual rate of fall of temperature when dry air is mixed up is 10° C/km. If, however, cloud is formed, the heat liberated or absorbed when the cloud droplets condense or evaporate, results in a fall of temperature with height in well mixed cloudy air of about half that in well mixed dry air. (The actual rate of fall of temperature in cloudy air depends on the temperature, since the amount of water vapour in saturated air increases rapidly with increasing temperature.)

The troposphere is a region where there is much vertical mixing of the air and the temperature is largely governed by this mixing. There are, however, many observed facts which indicate that absorption and emission of radiation are still important even here, but there is still much to be learnt about this.

As the outgoing terrestrial radiation travels on upwards, continually being absorbed and re-radiated, it comes to regions where, owing to the much smaller amounts of water vapour, its absorption is less strong. This will lead to a slower fall of temperature with height if the air is in 'radiative equilibrium', and finally the fall of temperature may be very slow indeed. In these conditions the air will be very stable and vertical mixing of the air will not be set up, and we may expect that the air will actually be in 'radiative equilibrium'. In this way the stratosphere is formed. Thus, in a very rough outline, we have a troposphere in which the air is mixed up, and the fall of temperature governed by the vertical mixing of the air, while at greater heights we have the stratosphere, where the fall of temperature is governed by the emission and absorption of long-wave radiation. In the upper part of the stratosphere the absorption of outgoing radiation will be small and much of it will escape into outer space.

We have accounted for a stratosphere where the fall of temperature with height is very slow, but, as we have seen earlier, there is frequently a marked *rise* of temperature above the tropopause in all parts of the world except during the polar winter. This rise of temperature is one of the many details which is not yet fully understood, but it would appear to be due, at least in part, to absorption by ozone of such solar ultra-violet radiation as has not already been absorbed at much greater heights.

It will be remembered that, when the warm region at a height of 50 km was first discovered, some people found it difficult to understand how the stratosphere could remain cold when sandwiched between the warm surface layers below and the 50-km warm region above, and we likened it to an unheated blanket which remained cold although sandwiched between two electrically heated blankets. The reason for this rather surprising temperature distribution is that the conditions in the stratosphere are quite different from those of one blanket between two other blankets. The stratosphere can radiate fairly easily directly out into space *through* the 50-km region because there is little water vapour there to absorb its radiation. Further, because of the small amount of water vapour, the warm region does not radiate much heat downwards that could be absorbed by the stratosphere (which is partly the reason why it *is* warm). It does radiate some heat, from the very small amount of water vapour, from the carbon dioxide, and from the ozone which it contains. This small amount of downward radiation from the 50-km warm region undoubtedly does warm the stratosphere a little, and is at least a partial cause of the rise of temperature in the first 10 km or so above the tropopause.

Finally, the necessarily rather long story may be briefly summed up as follows.

The air above 200 km is hot because of the absorption of very short-wave solar radiation and possibly of solar corpuscular radiation. At these high levels the temperature varies little with height because of the large effect of thermal conduction.

The 50-km region is warm because ozone absorbs somewhat longer ultra-violet wavelengths of sunlight which had not been absorbed by the highest atmosphere.

The ground is warm because it absorbs much of the main, visible part of sunlight, and this also warms the air at ground level.

The two intermediate regions are cold because they do not absorb much sunlight and they can get rid of such heat as they do absorb without having to be warmed to a high temperature.

4. THE STRATOSPHERE, THE TROPOPAUSE, AND THE TROPOSPHERE

The reader who only wants a general idea of the conditions in the atmosphere had better stop here, but those who wish to get some insight into scientific research may be interested in the following account of some of the difficulties which are encountered. Soon after the discovery of the stratosphere it was thought that the differences between the troposphere and stratosphere could be satisfactorily accounted for in the relatively simple manner that we have just described, but further observations have revealed facts that cannot be entirely explained in this simple way and it is now clear that many of our ideas will have to be somewhat changed, though at the present time we do not know exactly what these changes will be.

Today we do not even know how to define the tropopause in all cases. It is easy to define the stratosphere as the region in the middle atmosphere where the temperature remains nearly constant—or rises slightly—with increasing height; where, in consequence of this temperature distribution, the air is very stable and where there is no rapid, large-scale mixing by vertical movement of the air; where the moisture content of the air is very low, and where the ozone content is usually high. In the same way we can define the troposphere as the region in the lower atmosphere where, in general, the temperature falls with increasing height; where there is much mixing of the air by vertical motion; where nearly all the clouds and the 'weather' are found; where the air is generally fairly moist and where it is relatively weak in ozone. There is no doubt about the great difference between the troposphere and stratosphere, but when we come to define the tropopause we run into difficulties. In some cases the curve of temperature against height passes gradually from tropospheric to stratospheric conditions without any noticeable break, as in the curve shown for the polar winter in Fig. 2.1. In other cases there are several breaks, any one of which might be called the tropopause. At times the tropopause may appear to dissolve at one height and to reappear, perhaps a day later, at another height.

When it was first discovered that the air in the stratosphere was always very dry, it was hoped that the change of humidity with height might give some further information about the tropopause, but it was found that sometimes the air in the upper troposphere was also very dry and that the humidity showed no sudden change at the tropopause, even when this was strongly marked on the temperature curve. In the same way one might hope that the ozone content of the air might give some definite information but, as will be seen in Chapter 6, the ozone in the lower part of the stratosphere may be as low as that in the troposphere even when the tropopause is well marked. At the present time, for want of any better definition, the tropopause is usually defined as follows:

When the stratosphere begins as an abrupt change from falling to rising temperature, then the tropopause is the height of this change.

When the stratosphere begins as an abrupt change to a fall of less than 2° C/km or to a uniform temperature, then the tropopause is taken as the height of this change.

When there is no abrupt change in the rate of fall of temperature, the tropopause is taken as the height where the fall of temperature first drops to 2° C/km, provided that it does not exceed this value in any higher interval of one kilometre.

Clearly these rules are highly artificial and at times small differences of temperature, well within the errors of measurement, may cause a change in the adopted height of the tropopause of some kilometres.

So much for the difficulty of defining the tropopause. We are in equally great difficulties with the suggestion that the temperature of the stratosphere is governed by radiation, while that of the troposphere is governed by convection and mixing. Water vapour can only be removed from the atmosphere by cooling the air until it is supersaturated, when the water vapour condenses and falls out as rain, hail, or snow. The masses of very dry air that are sometimes found in the troposphere must, therefore, have been to very great heights where, owing to the low temperature, they lost their water vapour, and have descended again. From their water-vapour content we can tell how far they have descended. But we know that descending air is warmed 10° C for every kilometre that it has descended, owing to the effect of heating by compression. Measurements of the temperature of such masses of dry air show that they are indeed warmer than neighbouring air, but not nearly as warm as would be expected from the low water-vapour content. This can only be explained by supposing that heat has been lost by radiation from the air while it was descending in the troposphere, though we have previously supposed that the temperature was controlled by vertical movements and not by radiation.

Again in cyclonic conditions it is common to find very dry air in the upper troposphere and no discontinuity of humidity between the troposphere and the stratosphere, and that the air in the upper troposphere appears to have recently come down out of the stratosphere. Yet in these conditions the tropopause may be well defined by a sharp kink in the temperature curve and there may be a rise in the ozone concentration immediately on entering the stratosphere. It is very difficult to account for these apparent discordances. Clearly a case could be made out from these facts for saying that the whole of our theory of the troposphere and stratosphere is wrong; yet we believe that, in general, it is right and no better one has yet been suggested. No doubt, as a result of further study, we shall in time arrive at a true explanation of the temperature distribution in the atmosphere, but the reader may have gained some insight into the workings of scientific investigations from this account of the present difficulties. Thirty or forty years ago all seemed relatively simple, today further knowledge has shown that this is not so. Today our explanation of the warm region at a height of 50 km seems simple and adequate, but further investigation may show that this also needs revision. For the levels above 50 km we are still without adequate knowledge of the variations of temperature with latitude, season, and time of day, and we have no satisfactory explanation of the fact that the temperature at heights around 80 km in high temperate latitudes seems to be warmer in winter than in summer.

4. Cloud, Hail, and Rain

Es regnet wenn es regnen will,
es regnet seinen Lauf,
und wenn's genug geregnet hat,
so hört es wieder auf.

GOETHE

I. INTRODUCTION

THOUGH cloud, hail, rain, and snow probably affect human beings more closely than do other meteorological phenomena, to Goethe at any rate, the vagaries of rainfall appeared to be beyond human understanding! In recent years, however, we have really begun to get some knowledge of the physical processes by which these phenomena are caused. One reason for the more rapid progress is that aircraft have become available for meteorological studies and can carry observers and instruments up into the clouds. Before this it was very difficult to get information about the conditions inside clouds, since the type of observations which were necessary could not well be made with self-recording instruments carried on small balloons, nor could the balloons be brought into different parts of the cloud as required. Today an observer in an aircraft can fly backwards and forwards through different parts of a cloud and can measure the water content of the cloudy air, the number of cloud particles and the number of raindrops per unit volume, the number, shape, and size of ice crystals as well as the temperature at different heights. Research on clouds has also been greatly helped by the use of radar, both to locate the areas of rain within the cloud and also to fix the position of the exploring aircraft. Radio waves are scattered by all electrically conducting particles, but the amount of scattering depends very greatly on the size of the particles if, as in this case, they are smaller than the radio wavelength used. If there are two drops, one double the size of the other, then the larger drop will scatter radio waves sixty-four times more than the smaller drop. In this way it comes about that, although the cloud droplets are much more numerous than raindrops, yet rain, hail, and snow show up on the radar screen more readily that the cloud does. Hence it is possible by the use of radar to see a small volume of rain within a much larger mass of cloud. According to the way in which the radar is used, it is possible to show on the screen either a plan of the surrounding country within, say, 100 to 200 km around, on which the areas of rain are seen, or, alternatively, the radar can give a vertical section through the cloud, on which the position of the rain is shown. One can in this way find the height and position of rain, hail, or snow within a cloud.

2. RAIN

The question 'Why does this cloud give rain while that one does not?' may, at first sight, seem very simple and the answer given fifty years ago would probably have been that the first cloud contained more liquid water than the second, and that a cloud would naturally give rain when 'it contained more liquid water than it could hold'. Such an answer was never very satisfactory and we know that matters are much less simple than this, though we are still far from understanding the subject completely. The production of rain involves three separate stages:

   (i) the production of saturated, and finally supersaturated, air;
  (ii) the condensation of water vapour to form cloud droplets or ice crystals;
 (iii) the formation of raindrops from the myriads of very much smaller cloud droplets.

A. *Formation of Clouds*

Before water vapour will begin to condense in air to form cloud droplets, the air must become saturated and finally supersaturated (i.e. it must contain more water vapour than it can normally hold, or more strictly, the partial pressure of the water vapour in the air must be greater than that over a liquid water surface at the same temperature). In most cases of cloud formation this supersaturation is produced by the cooling of damp air. The amount of water vapour which can exist in a given volume of saturated air increases rapidly as the temperature rises. This is shown by the curved continuous line in Fig. 4.1.

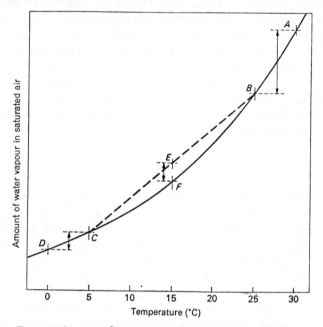

FIG. 4.1. Amount of water vapour in saturated air at different temperatures.

The continuous curved line shows the amount of water vapour in saturated air at different temperatures. The vertical distances *AB* and *CD* show the amount of water vapour which would condense out if the air were cooled 5° C starting at 30 or 5° C. The distance *EF* gives the amount of water vapour which would condense out if two equal masses of saturated air at 25 and 5° C respectively were mixed together.

It will be seen that if saturated air is cooled from 30 to 25° C a large amount of water vapour (equal to the vertical distance *AB*) must condense out, but if saturated air at a temperature of 5° C is cooled to 0° C only the amount equal to *CD* will condense out. This largely accounts for the fact that very high rates of rainfall are more common in warm than in cold climates.

The cooling of the air which leads to the formation of cloud in the atmosphere is nearly always due to the air rising, i.e.

moving from higher to lower pressure, so that the air expands. The cooling is a direct consequence of this expansion. (The allied, but opposite effect, i.e. warming by compression, may be demonstrated at any time by feeling the temperature of the bottom end of a pump after blowing up a tyre.)

B. *Types of Rising Currents*

There are four main causes which lead to rising air currents in the atmosphere and so to the production of cloud.

(i) The lower air near the ground may become so much warmer (and therefore lighter) than the air above, that 'bubbles' of damp, warm air may rise through their surroundings and form cumulus cloud. Such conditions are most frequently found on sunny days when the ground is strongly heated by sunshine. Naturally if the upper air is very cold and the surface air very warm, the rising currents are likely to be unusually strong, and in such conditions towering cumulus and cumulo-nimbus clouds will form. The essential factor in the formation of these 'bubble' clouds is that the lower air is too warm and the upper air too cold for the atmosphere to remain stable. The speed of the up-currents forming such cumulus clouds is usually of the order of a metre or two per second or, in the more extreme cases, ten or more metres per second.

(ii) Near the centre of cyclonic depressions and near warm fronts, air is found to be rising slowly over a very wide area. While a big cumulus cloud may cover an area of several square kilometres, the rising currents in depressions may cover thousands of square kilometres. Though much larger in area, the rate of rise of these latter currents is much smaller and is of the order of several centimetres per second rather than metres per second.

(iii) In the third case there are no individual rising currents at all, but there is a general mixing of the air at different levels due to turbulence or eddy motion caused by the winds. In this case the warm, damp air near the ground slowly diffuses upwards, mixing with the surrounding air all the time. This slow transport of water vapour upwards may or may not lead to the formation of a layer of cloud depending on the initial dampness of the air. Any cloud formed in this way usually consists of a relatively thin layer extending over a large area and little or no rain falls from it.

(iv) Finally, when the wind blows against a ridge of hills it is forced to rise, with consequent cooling and frequently with the formation of cloud. Everyone is familiar with the increase of cloud and rain in hilly districts. Clouds may also be formed by hills in a way which is less obvious than that due to the rising currents immediately over them. Nearly stationary waves may be set up in the general current of air blowing over a ridge of hills, and these waves may extend upwards to a height of several kilometres and may stretch for a long distance to leeward. If the air is damp enough lenticular, lozenge-shaped clouds may form at the crests of the waves. When the waves extend for many kilometres to leeward it is not obvious, at first sight, that there is any connection between the hills and the cloud. Since the position of the wave remains nearly stationary relatively to the hill, these clouds often appear to remain stationary, the air blowing through them; if they are carefully watched, small cloudlets may be seen forming at the windward edge, which gradually merge into the main cloud, while the cloud slowly evaporates at the leeward edge.

The cooling of air in rising currents is much the most important cause of the formation of cloud, but there is another process which may assist in the condensation of water vapour to form fog at ground level. In Fig. 4.1 the line showing the relation between the amount of water vapour in saturated air and the temperature is curved; it follows from this that if two equal masses of saturated (or nearly saturated) air at different temperatures (as represented by the points B and C in the diagram) are mixed together, the mixture will have the mean temperature and the mean water vapour content of the two individual masses (i.e. the point E in the diagram) but at this temperature the air is supersaturated, since it can only contain the amount of water vapour indicated by the point F. An amount of water vapour represented by the distance EF will therefore condense out as droplets to form fog. For the sake of clearness we have shown the mixing of two masses of air at very different temperatures (5 and 25° C) but normally in the atmosphere the two air masses will differ in temperature by only a few degrees, and it is easily seen that, as the two points B and C come closer together, the distance EF will rapidly diminish. For this reason very little rain can be produced by the mixing of two different air masses, but the process may be important in the formation of fog. Once fog has formed in the air, the extra outward radiation from it and consequent cooling may lead to thickening of the fog.

c. *Condensation of Water Vapour*

Having discussed the ways in which air may become saturated or supersaturated, so that condensation may begin to take place, we must now consider this process of condensation in some detail. Perfectly clean, damp air may be cooled to a temperature where it is supersaturated and yet no water droplets will be formed unless the supersaturation is very great. This is because extremely small droplets of water are unstable and, owing to their very small radius of curvature, they have a great tendency to evaporate, so that even if a small droplet was formed, it would quickly evaporate again unless the air was highly supersaturated. If, however, any particles are present in the supersaturated air, water vapour will begin to condense on them and since they are already fairly large, the water will not have so great a tendency to evaporate. Water drops may, therefore, begin to form on such particles as soon as the air becomes slightly supersaturated. If the particles—which may be solid or liquid—are hygroscopic, then water may begin to condense on them even before the air is quite saturated. These particles—known as condensation nuclei—are essential for the formation of cloud in the atmosphere. There is usually a very great number of condensation nuclei present in the atmosphere so that cloud forms as soon as the air is saturated. Even in the cleanest surface air there are usually many hundreds of condensation nuclei in every cubic centimetre, while in polluted air the numbers may go up to a hundred thousand or more. In the upper atmosphere the number of condensation nuclei is naturally smaller, but there is no evidence that cloud droplets are ever prevented from forming in the atmosphere by the lack of condensation nuclei. Condensation nuclei are produced by such processes as the evaporation of sea-spray and the combustion of fuel. Most combustion produces both solid smoke particles and also gases such as sulphur dioxide, the latter forming droplets of sulphurous or sulphuric acid which act as condensation nuclei.

The processes described above have been known for many years to apply in air whose temperature is above the freezing point, but until about 1940 it was generally believed that if air was below the freezing point then condensation would take place on other nuclei, called sublimation nuclei, and ice crystals would grow on them directly from the water vapour in the air. These sublimation nuclei were supposed to have a crystal structure similar to that of ice, so that ice crystals could easily grow on them. We now know that few, if any, substances normally found in nature are active in this way and that sublimation nuclei play no important part in the atmosphere. Except for condensation on existing ice crystals, water always first condenses on condensation nuclei to form liquid drops, even if the temperature is well below 0° C and these drops may, or may not, freeze later. In this way it comes about that clouds are often composed of liquid water drops although the temperature may be as low as −10° C.

D. *Freezing of Water Drops*

It is usual to think of water as freezing immediately it is cooled below 0° C; this is because we are generally dealing with fairly large volumes of water. When we come to deal with the minute volume of water in a cloud droplet we find that these droplets may often be cooled far below 0° C before they freeze. Just as water vapour must have some initial nucleus on which to condense, so liquid water must have some nucleus on which ice may begin to form. Such nuclei—called freezing nuclei— are far less numerous in the atmosphere than condensation nuclei. Freezing nuclei may be of different kinds and different freezing nuclei vary very much in their 'efficiency', this being shown by the amount of supercooling which is necessary before water will freeze on them, the most efficient nuclei requiring the least supercooling. Freezing nuclei on which ice will form at temperatures around −20° C are fairly plentiful, while there are only few nuclei so efficient that ice will form on them at temperatures as high as −15° C. Some exceptionally efficient nuclei will allow ice to form at temperatures around −6° C, the most efficient of these being silver iodide, about which we shall have more to say when we come to consider the question of the artificial stimulation of rain. The number of natural freezing nuclei in the atmosphere which are effective at any particular temperature thus increases as the temperature falls. Roughly speaking, at −25° C the number of effective freezing nuclei is some ten times as great as at −20° C, while at −30° C the number may be 100 times as great as at −20°. At a temperature of −40° C water seems to freeze spontaneously, even without the aid of freezing nuclei, and it is improbable that any natural water droplets in the atmosphere remain liquid at temperatures below −40° C. Very small drops of water are less likely to contain one of the rare, more efficient freezing nuclei than are larger drops, and for this reason very small drops can, in general be supercooled more than large drops (i.e. they will remain liquid at lower temperatures). A large volume of water, such as a cupful, will generally freeze at a temperature only just below 0° C. A minute crystal of ice is the perfect freezing nucleus and water will freeze on it as soon as the temperature falls very slightly below 0° C.

At 0° C the vapour pressure over a water surface is the same as that over an ice surface. As the temperature falls below 0° C the vapour pressure both over water and over ice decreases, but that over ice decreases the more rapidly, so that the vapour pressure over water becomes greater than that over ice, the difference being greatest at temperatures between about −5° and −25° C as shown in Fig. 4.2. If a cloud whose temperature is

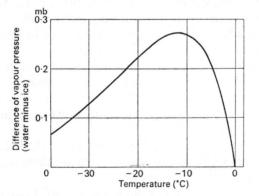

FIG. 4.2. Difference between the saturated vapour pressure over water and over ice at different temperatures.

below the freezing point consists partly of water droplets and partly of ice crystals, these two cannot exist together in equilibrium, but the water droplets will evaporate making the air supersaturated for ice, so that water vapour will then condense on ice crystals. The water will in this way be transferred from the droplets to the crystals, the drops evaporating and the crystals growing.

E. *Condensation Trails from Aircraft*

The exhaust from an aircraft engine discharges hot gases which contain both water vapour and condensation nuclei. When leaving the exhaust pipe the gases are so hot that the water vapour does not saturate them, but when the gases mix with the very cold surrounding air, saturation, and even supersaturation may be produced by the process of mixing, as shown in Fig. 4.1 and a cloud of water drops is formed. At the heights where condensation trails are usually formed, the temperature of the air is so low that most of the water drops freeze to form ice crystals. In those cases where very thick condensation trails are formed, it appears that the air was initially supersaturated with respect to ice but not with respect to water; no ice crystals were formed before the passage of the aircraft because there are no sublimation nuclei. When the droplets forming the cloud from the exhaust freeze, very large numbers of ice crystals are formed and some of the water vapour previously existing in the air will condense out on to them, in addition to the water from the exhaust gases, so forming a very dense trail. The gradual thickening of the trail by this process can often be seen for some little time after the passage of the aircraft.

The formation of condensation trails from aircraft thus illustrates several points which have been made above:

Though the air at great heights may be supersaturated with respect to ice, no cloud is formed because natural air contains no sublimation nuclei.

A water cloud is formed by the mixing of the hot, damp exhaust gases with the cold surrounding air, there being always plenty of condensation nuclei present.

The air temperature being around −40° C or lower, the water droplets can freeze without the assistance of freezing nuclei.

Water vapour in air which is supersaturated with respect to ice, but not to water, condenses to form ice crystals as soon as some minute ice crystals are present on which it can grow.

F. *Formation of Rain Drops*

The size of the droplets forming any cloud varies over a rather large range, clouds of the cumulus type having, on the average, larger droplets than clouds of the stratus type, but we may take the average diameter of a cloud droplet to be about 0·01 mm or rather more. Raindrops also vary in size but their average diameter is about 100 times that of the average cloud droplet, so that the volume of a raindrop is about a million times greater than that of a cloud droplet. This means that, on the average, a million cloud droplets must somehow collect together to form each raindrop. The crucial question which must be answered before we can say why a cloud produces rain, is how these million cloud droplets collect to form each raindrop. At the present time it is thought that the collection of many cloud droplets to form one raindrop may take place in two quite distinct ways: (i) by the coalescence of droplets on impact with each other; (ii) through the agency of ice crystals in supercooled clouds. We will consider each of these in turn.

(i) Cloud droplets, being very small, fall only slowly through the air and the chance of their colliding with one another, and of their consequent coalescence to form one larger drop, is rather small. If, however, there are a few larger droplets present in the cloud they will fall faster than the rest, and will have more chance of colliding and coalescing with smaller droplets, and so growing as they fall. This will give them a still greater chance of striking other droplets and so of growing in size continuously. However, before they can pick up enough cloud droplets to grow into raindrops, they must clearly fall through a great depth of cloud, so that rain could only be produced in this way from thick, deep clouds.

(ii) There is, however, another way in which raindrops may be formed from cloud droplets. We have seen that if both ice crystals and water droplets are present together in the same cloud at a temperature below 0° C, then the water drops will evaporate and the ice crystals will grow, so transferring the water from the droplets to the ice crystals. Let us now consider the case of a cumulus cloud in which there are rising currents with speeds of a few metres per second. The lower part of the cloud will consist of water droplets, provided that the temperature of the air is higher than about −10° C. At higher altitudes, where the temperature is between −20 and −30° C, some of the droplets will probably freeze. As soon as there are both ice crystals and supercooled water droplets present together in the cloud, the ice crystals will begin to grow, while the water drops will evaporate. The growing ice crystals will fall through the cloud of small droplets and whenever they touch a supercooled droplet, the droplet will freeze on to the falling crystal. The falling ice crystal now continue to grow by the coalescence process. When the crystal falls into the region where the temperature is above 0° C it will melt to form a raindrop.

At one time it was thought that the collection of cloud droplets into raindrops by the coalescence process would be so slow a process that it would have little effect in producing rain, and that the second process, involving supercooled droplets and ice crystals, was more important. However, careful observations have shown that heavy rain can fall from clouds whose temperature is everywhere above the freezing point, so that this rain must, presumably, be formed by the coalescence process. It now seems probable that both these processes give rise to the formation of rain, so that the requirements for a cloud to give rain are:

(i) a thick and deep layer of cloud;
(ii) *either* the upper part of the cloud must have a temperature below −10 to −15° C so that ice crystals are formed (unless, as sometimes happens, crystals fall into the cloud from other, higher clouds);

or there must be a few relatively large nuclei in the cloud on which abnormally large cloud droplets will grow, and which will fall sufficiently fast to collide with many other cloud droplets. Only if these conditions are satisfied will the cloud give rain.

g. *The Cold Box Experiment*

At this stage it may be useful to describe a striking experiment which is fairly easy to perform and which illustrates very clearly the principles which have been set out in the above discussion. A metal box about 30 cm across is fixed in another box a few centimetres larger. Both boxes are open-ended and are fixed with their open ends upwards, while the space between

them is filled with petroleum or some other suitable liquid that
may be cooled by putting solid carbon dioxide ('dry ice') into it.
As the outer space is cooled, so the air in the inner box will be
cooled also, and the cold air, being heavy, will stay in the bottom
of the box. When the air in the inner box has been cooled to
$-5°$ C or lower, it will be found that on breathing into the box,
a fog is formed. If the inside of the box is painted black and
a strong beam of light is shone into it, the fog will be seen very
clearly and the myriads of minute droplets will be just visible.
This fog, which consists of liquid water droplets, has a rather dull
appearance and will remain stable for some time, since the
droplets are so small that they will fall out only slowly.

We now take a small piece of solid carbon dioxide (whose
temperature is about $-79°$ C) in a pair of forceps and move it
around in the foggy air for a few seconds. Immediately a complete change in the appearance of the fog begins to take place.
In addition to the rather dull fog of water droplets, minute ice
crystals will begin to be seen shining brilliantly in the beam of
light. Very soon it will be noticed that the fog is rapidly disap-
pearing and that the growing ice crystals are falling out, until
before long the air in the cold box is quite clear. The experiment
may now be repeated again by breathing into the cold box as
before. Time must, however, be allowed for *all* the ice crystals
to fall out, otherwise the new water fog will begin to disappear
as soon as it is formed. The experiment is very striking and if
the temperatures are carefully measured useful scientific information can be obtained by this type of experiment. Thus if,
instead of moving a piece of solid carbon dioxide about in the
foggy air to cause the formation of ice crystals, we used a piece
of metal cooled to various known temperatures, we could find
the highest temperature at which water drops just froze in the
absence of freezing nuclei and confirm that it is about $-40°$ C.

We will now consider how this experiment illustrates the
principles set out above.

(i) Fog is formed by the mixture of two masses of damp air at
different temperatures. The cold air in the box will be almost
saturated and when we breathe into it we mix warm, nearly
saturated air with the cold damp air and produce supersaturation (see Fig. 4.1);

(ii) Because there are no freezing nuclei that are effective at the temperature of the air in the box (say $-5°$ C), the excess water vapour will condense on condensation nuclei, and will remain as liquid droplets although the temperature is several degrees below the freezing point;

(iii) Supercooled water freezes even in the absence of freezing nuclei if cooled below $-40°$ C. Solid carbon dioxide has a temperature of about $-79°$ C and any air that comes into close contact with it will be cooled well below $-40°$ C, so that the water droplets which are formed can freeze immediately;

(iv) Ice particles tend to grow in size in the presence of supercooled water drops, while the water drops evaporate. The rapid clearing of the fog, as soon as ice particles are formed in it, shows that the water drops evaporate, while the falling of the ice crystals shows that these have grown large at the expense of the much more numerous water drops.

H. *Drizzle*

If raindrops are to be formed by either of the two processes described in section F above, a rather deep cloud layer must be present. When the cloud is not deep enough to allow rain to be formed, the growing droplets may fall out of the bottom of the cloud as drizzle before they can grow into raindrops. These droplets which have a diameter of about 0·1 mm may, or may not, evaporate before they reach the ground.

I. *Cloudbursts*

Occasionally quite exceptionally heavy falls of rain occur which, fortunately, generally only last a few minutes, but they may do much damage in that short time. In big cumulo-nimbus clouds the speed of the up-currents may be so large that it is impossible for rain to fall through them. The rate at which a raindrop will fall through the air increases with the size of the drop, but when its diameter is about 5 mm its shape begins to be distorted by the pressure of the air against it and still larger drops are broken up by the air pressure into smaller drops. The maximum rate of fall before the drops break up is about 10 m/s, and if the up-current in a cloud has a speed greater than this, no rain can fall through it, but all the water will be held on the top of the rising current and very large amounts of liquid water may accumulate. When the speed of the up-current falls off, all this water will fall together, giving extremely heavy rain for a short time.

3. GLAZED FROST, RIME, AND HOAR FROST

Before discussing these subjects it may be useful if we stop here for a moment to consider exactly what happens when water freezes. When water at $0°$ C freezes to form ice at the same temperature a large amount of heat is released (just as a large amount of heat must be supplied to a block of ice at $0°$ C to cause it to melt to form water at the same temperature). If a drop of supercooled water is inoculated with a minute ice crystal, it will immediately begin to freeze and the heat released by the freezing of part of the drop will warm the rest of the drop until the whole (partly ice and partly water) is at a temperature of $0°$ C. Only after the removal of more heat will the whole of the drop become ice.

A. *Glazed Frost*

If rain formed in relatively warm air at the cloud level falls through a layer of very cold air near the ground, the drops may be supercooled when they arrive at the surface of the earth. When such a supercooled drop of rain strikes the cold ground or the twig of a tree it will begin to freeze, but, as explained above because of the heat released on freezing, the whole of the drop will warm up to $0°$ C and the liquid part will spread out over the ground or the twig, and only when more heat is removed from it will this water freeze, forming a layer of clear ice over the ground or the twig. It is in this way that the ground and trees become coated with a layer of clear ice or glazed frost.

B. *Rime*

Cloud droplets and fog droplets are very much smaller than raindrops and when, on a very cold, foggy night, supercooled fog droplets drift against the twigs of a tree they immediately begin to freeze in the same way as we described for raindrops, but, because of their very small size, the heat released on freezing can be quickly conducted away either to the cold twig or to the cold air, so that the whole droplet will freeze very rapidly and will not spread out over the twig as in the case of the raindrop but will solidify more or less as it touches the twig. As more and more cold fog droplets strike the twig they will build up a mass of porous ice or rime, with many air spaces between the solidified droplets. It is the fact that rime contains these air spaces which reflect light that make it appear white in contrast to glazed frost which is clear, solid ice.

c. Dew and Hoar Frost

On a clear, cold night blades of grass, twigs of trees, etc. are strongly cooled owing to loss of heat by outward radiation and are likely to be below the temperature of the surrounding air. As soon as a blade of grass is cooled below the temperature at which the surrounding air is saturated (i.e. the dew point), water vapour will begin to be deposited on it. If the air temperature is above the freezing point, the condensed water will remain liquid as drops of dew. There has been some discussion as to whether dew can give enough water to be of use to plants, and the answer seems to be that it depends very much on the conditions. A long time ago an experiment was made in Britain, in which a sod was isolated, weighed, and replaced in the ground in the evening, and then weighed again in the morning. In the morning, even though it had a heavy deposit of dew, the sod has lost weight since the previous evening. It seems that more water had evaporated from the sod than was deposited on the grass as dew; in fact much of the dew probably came from the water which had evaporated from the soil beneath. This, however, need not necessarily be the case and in other conditions more water may be deposited than is evaporated, though possibly not more than is evaporated during the whole 24 hours.

If the temperature is much below $0°$ C the drops of dew will begin to freeze since, unlike droplets condensing in the free air, they will probably contain some freezing nuclei from the grass blades etc. As soon as a speck of ice has formed, further ice crystals will grow directly on the ice nucleus without the formation of liquid water drops. We thus find on a cold morning that the grass is covered with a feathery structure of loose ice crystals, or hoar frost, which reflect light from all their surfaces and so appear white.

4. HAIL

It has been shown above that when the temperature is below
0° C ice may form on grass, trees, etc. in three different ways:
  (i) Ice crystals may grow on twigs, etc. directly from the
      water vapour in the air (hoar frost).
 (ii) If supersaturated droplets are very small they may freeze
      solid almost immediately they touch a solid object and
      will build up a mass of porous soft ice (rime).
(iii) If the supercooled water drops are large, the latent heat
      which is liberated when the water freezes will prevent the
      whole drop freezing immediately and liquid water will
      spread over any object it touches and then freeze as a
      layer of clear ice (glazed frost).
Each of these processes takes place in clouds giving rise respectively to snow, soft hail, and hard hail.

Very big, towering cumulo-nimbus clouds, such as thunderstorms, seem to be necessary for the formation of a heavy
shower of hard hail. Indeed it is obvious that very strong up-
currents must be present to hold up the hailstones in the cloud
while they are growing, and also that there must be much liquid
water, whose temperature is at, or below, the freezing point,
from which the hailstones can grow. According to our present
knowledge it seems that a hailstone grows from an ice crystal
which, falling through supercooled cloud droplets, grows at
first in the form of rime and becomes a particle of soft hail. (It
is usually found that hailstones have a core of soft, white ice.)
If later, this particle of soft ice is caught in a strong up-current
and carried into a region where there is much supercooled
rain, then layers of clear ice will form on it, as in glazed frost.
Big cumulo-nimbus clouds consist of many distinct rising currents and if, after growing and falling out of one up-draught,
the hailstone is picked up by another, it will continue to receive successive coatings of clear ice until it is finally able to
fall out of the cloud.

While the account of the formation of hail given above is
probably correct in general, many details are still not known,
particularly why some hailstones grow to an excessive size.
Again in America, severe thunderstorms are about equally
common on the Florida coast and in the central plains; hail,

however, is much more common in the central plains than on the coast. Again, spring and early summer thunderstorms are more likely to give hail than equally severe storms in the late summer and autumn, though exceptionally large stones are more frequent in the latter season. Until we can say why there should be these differences, we are clearly a long way from completely understanding how hail is formed.

5. ICING ON AIRCRAFT

The presence of supercooled cloud droplets and raindrops in the atmosphere may cause serious difficulties for aircraft. When an aeroplane flies through clouds whose temperature is below the freezing point, any liquid drops will begin to freeze when they strike it. In certain cases the rate at which ice accumulates on the aircraft may be very rapid and, in addition to the increase in weight, it may destroy the aerodynamic efficiency of the wings and propellor, or block the intake of the engine. When flying through supercooled clouds whose droplets are very small, a porous mass of white ice may be formed, as already described under the heading of rime. When flying through supercooled raindrops of relatively large size, these larger drops will not all freeze immediately they touch the aircraft but, as described under glazed frost, only some of the water will freeze while the rest will remain liquid until enough heat can be removed to allow this to freeze also. In this latter case a layer of clear, hard ice may form which is much more difficult to remove than the white, porous deposit. Aircraft which are likely to fly through these icing conditions are therefore fitted with some de-icing system which either prevents ice forming or breaks it off as it forms.

6. ARTIFICIAL CONTROL OF WEATHER

The processes taking place in the atmosphere are on so vast a scale that, for the most part, there is no hope of influencing them by any artificial means. Amounts of energy greater than those released by atomic explosions would be required. There are, however, a few cases in which attempts to modify the weather may have some chance of success and be economically possible; these include the artificial increase of rain over relatively small areas, the local clearing of fog and the prevention of damaging hailstorms. (The possible change of climate which might be effected by the suggested flooding of great areas of desert is outside the scope of this book.)

A. *Artificial Increase of Rainfall*

In many parts of the world the economic value of even a small increase in the rainfall, at the right time of the year, would be so great that much research has been carried out on the possibility of producing such an increase. We may say at once that there is no foreseeable way of producing rain in conditions with cloudless skies, but there does seem to be a reasonable possibility of producing rain, or increasing the amount of rain, in cloudy conditions by assisting the collection of cloud droplets into raindrops. This implies that the existing conditions must be such as nearly to produce rain, and it is therefore a matter of great difficulty to assess the exact value of the artificial rain-producing operations, and it is easy to produce figures which indicate quite extravagant successes.

It has been shown that some million cloud droplets must collect together to form each raindrop, and that the two most probable ways in which this may occur in nature are: (i) through the action of ice particles in supercooled clouds, and (ii) through the more rapid rate of fall of a few larger particles that may naturally exist in the cloud and that coalesce with smaller droplets on impact. If the conditions at any time are such that the formation of rain from thick cloud is prevented by lack of minute ice crystals or a few larger particles, then increased rainfall might be produced by supplying the one or the other, according to the temperature. Up to the present time most of the work has been done on supercooled clouds, by seeding them either with solid carbon dioxide dropped into the cloud in order to form large numbers of ice particles, or with silver iodide crystals which cause freezing of supercooled water drops at temperatures below about $-6°$ C. There is no doubt that if the upper part of a large cumulus cloud is well below $0°$ C and yet is not giving rain, then a marked effect can be produced by seeding it with either solid carbon dioxide or silver iodide. Usually an appreciable amount of rain is seen to fall out of the bottom of such a cloud and this rain may, or may not, reach the ground before it evaporates. At the same time a change comes over the appearance of the cloud as the supercooled water droplets change to ice crystals. In those cases where the whole of the cloud is above 0° C, so that there can never be any ice crystals, finely powdered common salt may be dropped into the cloud to assist the formation of some larger droplets.

We do not know how frequently, or in which particular cases, the production of rain from an apparently suitable cloud is prevented by the lack of ice nuclei or of a few large particles, since extremely few such particles or nuclei are required (only about one per cubic metre) and it is difficult to observe such scarce particles. It is therefore, very difficult to estimate how frequently artificial action might increase the rainfall by an economically significant amount. Favourable conditions are thought to be found in some mountain regions where there is normally much cloud, but where the cloud does not give much rain.

An advantage of a quite different kind might be obtained by seeding supercooled clouds of the layer type with solid carbon dioxide from aircraft. The result of seeding such clouds (generally stratus or strato-cumulus) is to clear the cloud in exactly the same way as the fog was cleared in the 'cold box' experiment. As a result of such seeding, a clear lane is produced along the track of the seeding aircraft which often becomes a few kilometres wide. This widening is possibly due to the formation of secondary ice crystals by the breaking up of the growing primary crystals. The persistence of thick layer-clouds over a city in winter gives rise to a very dark, gloomy day, and clearing such cloud might be of economic value in saving electricity for light, as well as improving the amenities for the population. The seeding would have to be done continuously, or at least at frequent intervals, since the cloudy air would drift over and also the cleared lanes would slowly fill in again. Unfortunately in temperate latitudes the cloud layer is mostly too warm for this clearing to be possible.

B. *Clearing of Fog*

It is quite impracticable to clear fog on a large scale on account of the enormous amount of energy required, but it is possible to clear a limited area. Experiments on clearing small areas have been made with a view to clearing the runways of aerodromes. The method generally employed is to heat the air until the fog droplets evaporate, but in order to clear even such a limited area, very large amounts of fuel are necessary. This is not because so much heat is required to evaporate the fog droplets, but rather because it is necessary to warm up a very large mass of air. Further, even in foggy conditions there is nearly always a slight wind which drifts more foggy air across the runway as soon as it has been cleared, so that the heating must be continued, requiring yet further amounts of fuel. It is somewhat tantalizing that just above the cold foggy air there may exist warm, dry air which, if it could be mixed with the air below, would immediately clear the fog. Unfortunately again enormous amounts of power would be necessary to effect this mixing.

c. *Prevention of Damaging Hailstones*

On account of the damage done to crops and glass-houses by large hailstones, many attempts have, in the past, been made to ward off destructive storms. Most of these have been made without any basis of scientific knowledge about the formation of hail, and it is not surprising that such methods as the ringing of bells have produced little effect! Fortunately only some storms give damaging hail and when we know more about its formation it may be possible to take artificial action to reduce its occurrence. The most hopeful line of attack seems to be to cause the hail to fall as many small stones rather than as a few big ones. One method which has been tried with this end in view is to seed the lower parts of the growing cloud with crystals of silver iodide by the use of rockets. (It will be remembered that silver iodide has the property of aiding the formation of ice in supercooled water.) A second suggestion, also using rockets, is to seed the growing cloud with finely powdered common salt on which water drops, larger than the average, will form, since it is thought that only the relatively few large droplets in the base of the cloud grow into hailstones. Here again the object is to produce a large number of small hailstones rather than a few large ones. At the present time it is quite uncertain whether any of these methods will be effective, but at least they are based on the best knowledge of the growth of hailstones which is at present available.

5. Thunderstorms

As in the case of the other researches on the physics of clouds which were described in Chapter 4, both radar and aircraft have been of great assistance in the exploration of thunderstorms. Although the air in thunderstorms is very turbulent, aircraft fitted with various instruments have made numerous flights through thunder clouds and, since the position of the aircraft, as well as the position of the heaviest rain can be seen on the radar screen, the aircraft can be directed by radio into the most active part of the storm. ('Pity the poor pilot' one remarked!) Many measurements can be made from aircraft which would be almost impossible to make by the use of instruments carried up on small balloons. Measurements of the height of the aircraft show how much it is carried up or down by vertical currents, and so the strength of the vertical currents can be estimated. In addition to measuring the temperature of the air and making observations of rain, hail, or snow, the amount of liquid water in the cloud and the electrical conditions are also measured. Many studies of thunderstorms have also been carried out at high-level mountain observatories when they are surrounded by a thunder cloud. From all these studies it is now possible to give the following picture of a typical thunderstorm.

A thunder cloud, which is a typical large cumulo-nimbus, consists of one or more cells, or units, with fairly well-defined air circulations and life-histories. Small, isolated thunderstorms of the April-shower type may consist of a single cell, while larger storms may have many adjacent cells in different stages of development. Each cell may be some 10 km wide and 10 km high, and have a lifetime of the order of an hour. In large storms there will be growing cells, mature cells giving rain and lightning, and old, decaying cells. In the early stages of its growth a cell consists throughout of rising air currents which form cumulus cloud at their tops, though the rising currents are often not uniform but have local areas of more vigorously rising air. This can be well seen if a cumulo-nimbus cloud is watched from a distance, when first one towering mass of cloud will be seen bulging upwards from the main mass, only to die away within a few minutes, while another tower pushes up in an adjacent part of the cloud. In this way the cloud builds up until its top is some 10 km or more high.

Now the second stage of the cell's development begins and rain will be seen for the first time on the radar screen or by the aircraft flying in the cloud. Soon after this the first lightning occurs. By this time the cell contains both strong up-currents and strong down-currents, the latter being partly due to the fact that air is carried down by the falling rain and hail. In the final stage of the cell, the up-currents cease and only down-currents are left, while the heavy rain and hail also stop and the cell gradually dies away.

In the early stages, when there are rising currents in the cell, air will be drawn in at the bottom, so that the surface wind will tend to blow towards the storm, while in the later stage, when down-draughts are found, the surface wind may blow outwards from the storm. For this reason the surface wind is not a good indication of the direction of movement of the storm; this movement is more closely given by the direction of the wind at a height of about 3 km. Except in some rare cases to be discussed later, the temperature of the upper part of the cloud is well below 0° C by the time the second stage is reached. The measurements show that up-draughts with a speed of 30 m/s are often found. When watching a large thunderstorm it will often be noticed that one area of intense rain and lightning will die out and another, in a different part of the cloud, will become active as one cell decays and another reaches maturity. This is a further reason why it is difficult to say from the ground in which direction the storm is moving.

In an active thunder cloud hail or snow is nearly always present, together with liquid water drops; we shall see that this fact has great significance when we come to discuss the way in which the electric charges are produced. Liquid water drops have been observed nearly 3 km above the freezing level, where the temperature must have been around $-20°$ C or lower. As was seen in Chapter 4 (see glazed frost), when water vapour is condensing fast, it is possible for ice and liquid water to exist together, and the hail may be coated with liquid water even when the air temperature is far below the freezing point. This is because the freezing of the water releases heat and the water can only freeze as fast as it can lose this heat to the surrounding cold air. An active thunder cloud is always very deep and often extends nearly up to the tropopause, indeed it seems that some very big storms may even penetrate the tropopause. Lightning does not generally occur unless the top of the cloud reaches a height where the temperature is below $-20°$ C.

2. THE ELECTRIC CHARGES

One of the first things which we want to know about a thunderstorm is the position of the positive and negative charges within the cloud and it is surprising that it was not until 1937 that this apparently simple question was finally settled. Until then there had been much discussion as to whether a thunder cloud had a positive charge at the top and a negative charge at the bottom or vice versa. It might be supposed that this could have easily been settled by making measurements on the ground of the sign of the electric field as a thunderstorm passed overhead. However, the electric field below even the ideally simple thunderstorm shown in Fig. 5.1 (*a*) is rather complicated, being directed downwards immediately under the centre of the cloud, upwards a little further out, and downwards again at a distance from the storm. In a real thunderstorm, with several centres of charge (see Fig. 5.1 (*b*)), it is almost impossible to infer the position of the charges overhead from measurements made on the ground. There is also a considerable 'space charge'—i.e. an electric charge in the clear air between the cloud and the ground—which makes the electric field at ground level still more complex. We shall see later that there is also a positive electric field in the air at places nowhere near a thunderstorm, even in fine weather.

This elementary question of the sign of the electric charges near the top and the bottom of a thunder cloud was finally settled when very small, simple instruments were sent up into a

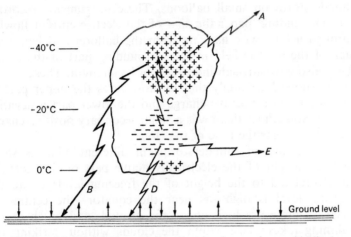

FIG. 5.1 (*a*). Distribution of the electric charges in an idealized thunderstorm.

The arrows at ground level show the direction of the electric field at the surface of the earth due to the charges in the thunder cloud. The paths of some possible lightning discharges are also shown.

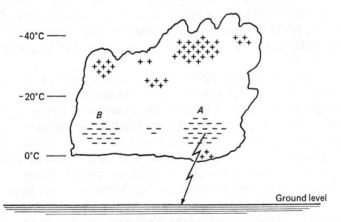

FIG. 5.1 (*b*). Possible distribution of the electric charges in a real thunderstorm.

Average temperatures of the air at different heights are shown on the left of the diagrams.

thunderstorm on small balloons. These instruments recorded on 'pole-finding' paper the sign of the electric current flowing through a long wire hanging from the balloon and hence the sign of the electric field in the surrounding part of the cloud. They also gave a rough indication of its strength. These instruments showed definitely that in most cases the upper part of the cloud had a positive charge and the lower part a negative charge. Sometimes there was a small secondary positive charge right down near the base of the cloud.

Observations of thunderstorms in different climates show that the height of the electrically active part of the storm is closely related to the height of the freezing level; where the freezing level is high—as near the equator—the centres of electric charge are high above the ground, and much of the lightning takes place within the clouds without striking the ground. Where the freezing level is low—as in temperate latitudes, particularly in winter—the electric charges are also low and many of the lightning flashes come down to the ground, so that often more damage is done by lightning in the small storms of temperate regions than in the much more spectacular storms of low latitudes. In England about half the lightning flashes strike the ground and about half are within the clouds. As a rough generalization, we may say that the lower negative charge is generally situated at a height where the temperature is about $-5°$ C, while the positive charge may be 3 km or more higher. The charged centre in a cloud has a diameter of the order of 1 or 2 km.

The quantity of electricity in each centre of charge is generally between 10 and 50 Coulombs, i.e. the amount of electricity which would pass through a wire carrying a current of 1 A in 10–50 s. This amount may seem surprisingly small in view of the violence of a flash, but as it all passes in a very short time, the flash may carry a current of many thousands of amperes. The electric fields in thunderstorms as measured by aircraft flying in the clouds are of the order of 1000 to 2000 V/cm. As might be expected, smaller clouds producing no lightning may also have quite large electric fields provided that they give rain, but clouds giving no rain seem to have little electric charge.

3. LIGHTNING

A. *The General Structure of a Lightning Flash*

Lightning is proverbially quick, but in point of fact one complete flash may last for more than a second. When watching a large thunderstorm in the distance it is often noticeable that some flashes flicker for an appreciable time. Again atmospherics heard on a radio set—which, of course, are caused by lightning—often consist of a series of crackles lasting for a second or more, showing that the flash is by no means instantaneous. Actually what is seen as one flash may really consist of a series of many separate strokes, separated in time by a tenth to a fifth of a second, and all following one another down the same path. While the interval of time between individual strokes is too short for the eye to distinguish them individually, the different strokes can easily be separated on a photograph taken at night by keeping the camera swinging horizontally, so that the strokes, which are spaced out in time, appear to be spaced out in distance on the photograph. Occasionally such a photograph taken with a moving camera will show that the path of the lightning glows faintly between two strokes, and during this time a small electric current continues to flow down the path for, perhaps, a tenth of a second so that although the current is small compared to that in the brighter parts of the flash, the total negative charge carried down to earth may be large.

B. *The Electric Current in Lightning Flashes*

The maximum current in a lightning flash can be measured in several ways, but the simplest and most direct is to fix near a lightning conductor a bundle of iron strips, which will become magnetized when an electric current flows through the lightning conductor and will retain their magnetism. Then, by measuring the magnetism of the strips after the conductor has been struck, it is possible to deduce the maximum current which flowed through the conductor. The currents found in this way vary considerably but are very large—as much as 10 000 to 100 000 A—though the total charge passed may be only 10–20 C. While the total duration of a complete flash may be as long as a second, the time during which the main current in one stroke is flowing is less than 1/10 000 s, which accounts for the very large current in a flash. From the study of thunderstorms it is also possible to estimate the difference of electrical potential which may exist between the thunder cloud and the ground; this may be well over 100 000 000 V, so that each flash represents the dissipation of a very large amount of electrical energy, and even a moderate storm may well be producing electrical energy equivalent to 1000 MW—about the same as that produced by a large electric power station. Though this seems a very large amount of electrical energy, the mechanical energy of the thunderstorm, i.e. that of the winds, rain, etc., is far greater. This is another example of the enormous energy involved in many atmospheric processes.

c. *Structure of Individual Lightning Flashes*

We have described earlier how the individual strokes of a compound lightning flash may be separated out in a photograph, by swinging the camera from side to side during the exposure. The detailed structure of an individual stroke may be found in a similar way, but now far higher speeds and far shorter times are involved and a special camera must be used for the purpose. The results of these observations are so interesting that we shall describe the method in some detail. Several types of camera have been used, but one of the simplest and most successful is sketched in Fig. 5.2 (*a*). A light wheel with a flat rim has a ciné film fixed round the rim and the wheel is revolved in a horizontal plane at a high speed by a motor. The revolving wheel is in a light-tight box and a camera lens is fixed in the side of the box so as to throw a picture of the landscape on to the ciné film. Another camera has an exactly similar lens but has a stationary film. The cameras are used at night and are pointed in the direction of a thunderstorm

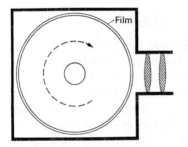

FIG. 5.2 (*a*). Principle of the camera with rapidly rotating film used for studying the structure of lightning flashes.

with the lenses left open until a flash appears within the field of view of the cameras. The films are then changed ready for the next photograph.

When a flash takes place, a streak, or dart of light travels down from the cloud to the ground. Let us consider how this will appear in the pictures of the flash. Consider first the stationary film and suppose that the bright dart moves straight down from the cloud to the ground. This will clearly produce a straight line, as *AB* in Fig. 5.2 (*b*). Now consider the moving film; when the bright dart first appears below the cloud it will

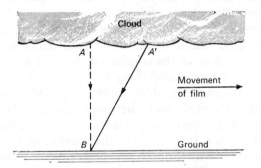

Fig. 5.2 (*b*). Diagram showing the method of measuring the speed of a lightning flash using a camera with moving film.

form an image on the film at *A*, but as the bright dart moves downwards the film also moves sideways, and by the time the dart reaches the ground and forms an image at *B*, the point *A* on the film will have moved to *A'*, so on the moving film the bright dart will produce the sloping line *A'B*. The only difference between the pictures of the flash on the stationary and moving films is due to the relative speed of the film and of the bright dart. By comparing the two pictures it is possible to measure the speed at which the bright dart moved down from the cloud to the ground. The fact that an actual lightning flash may have a zigzag course instead of a straight one makes no difference to the measurements. Many flashes are branched and the movement of the bright dart along each branch can be measured in the same way.

A study of many lightning flashes between cloud and ground by such methods as that just described shows that (except in the case of the first stroke of a compound flash, which will be discussed later) each stroke starts downwards from the cloud as a bright dart moving with a speed of rather over 2000 km/s and so taking about 1/1000 s to reach the ground. This bright dart carries negative electricity from the cloud downwards and leaves highly ionized air in its wake. Note that though the dart leaves highly ionized air in the whole channel between the cloud and the ground, yet the whole channel does not continuously give out light while the bright dart is travelling downwards; if the channel were continuously illuminated, then photographs such as the sketch in Fig. 5.2 (b) would show a wide ribbon of light in the region ABA', and not the sharp line $A'B$.

When the downward moving bright dart reaches the ground, and the electric charge in the cloud becomes connected with the ground by way of the conducting channel which the dart left behind it, a remarkable thing happens. At this moment an exceedingly bright stroke starts to move upwards following the same ionized channel. Both the brightness and speed of this upward stroke are very great and this part of the flash carries the largest current. Its speed is of the order of 40 000 km/s and so it covers the distance between the ground and the cloud in about 1/20 000 s. The electric current carried by this part of the flash may be between 10 000 and 100 000 A, negative electricity being transferred downwards. If there are further strokes in the same compound flash, the processes described above are repeated.

In the above description we limited ourselves to the second and subsequent strokes of a compound lightning flash, purposely excluding the first stroke, since the first stroke differs in some ways from the later strokes. We will now consider this first stroke. Like the subsequent strokes it also consists of two separate parts, a slow, downward-moving dart and a bright, upward-moving return stroke. The initial downward-moving dart of subsequent strokes was able to follow the path of former strokes, owing to some ionization still remaining in the channel. On the other hand, the downward-moving dart of the first stroke has to make its way through un-ionized air, and it is probably for this reason that it is different from the later one. The actual dart is so faintly luminous that it has not been photographed and its presence is inferred, as we shall describe. Its speed is far slower than that of subsequent darts, being only about 200 km/s as against 2000 km/s for the darts of subsequent strokes. When it has travelled downwards some 20 to 30 m its path suddenly lights up momentarily so that it can be photographed, then it travels another 20 to 30 m and again this part of its path lights up momentarily, and so it progresses downwards. What is seen in the photographs from the camera with moving film is a series of bright steps and we infer that there must have been a downward-moving dart, too faint to be photographed, travelling slowly down from the cloud to the ground, and that every 20 or 30 m the path behind it is suddenly lit up sufficiently to be photographed. The details of this process are still not well understood. The whole of this part of the flash takes about $\frac{1}{100}$ s, far longer than the corresponding time for subsequent strokes. As soon as the dart reaches the ground a very bright return stroke starts upwards as in subsequent strokes.

D. *Branching*

Photographs of lightning frequently show flashes with many branches, mostly directed downwards towards the ground. This branching is nearly always limited to the first stroke of a compound flash, the later strokes following only that branch which hits the ground. The branching is started by the first slow-moving dart as it makes its way downwards through the un-ionized air. At times this first dart divides into two, each part forming a separate branch. This may happen several times and many branches are formed. These branches grow outwards and downwards and finally one of them usually hits the ground. During this part of the stroke negative electricity flows down from the charged cloud and is distributed in the air along the channel formed by the dart. As soon as one of the branches hits the ground, and electrical connection is established between the cloud and the ground, the intense and brilliant stroke starts upwards. When this intense upward stroke reaches the junction with a branch, it also divides into two, one part continuing upwards along the main channel, while the other part follows the original dart, still moving downwards along its branch, until, owing to the greater speed of the return stroke, it catches up with the dart. The same thing happens at the junction with each branch and finally the intense upward stroke reaches the cloud and the ends of all the branches. During this part of the flash the remaining electricity in that part of the cloud from which the flash started and all the negative charge which had been carried down by the original slow-moving dart from the cloud and distributed in the air along the branches is finally transferred down to the ground. It should be noted that although the bright return stroke moves upwards it still transfers negative electricity downwards, as in the case of the downward moving dart.

E. *Origin of Multiple Strokes*

It often happens that there is a second centre of negative charge such as B in Fig. 5.1 (b) in the cloud at some distance from the charge A which started the first stroke. After the first stroke, the part of the cloud around A will be discharged and will be nearly at the potential of the ground, so that there may now be a large difference of potential between A and B which may initiate a second stroke. However, since there is no pre-existing ionized channel in the air between A and B, the slow-moving type of dart must first make its way from B to A or more probably a slightly different type of dart moves from A to B. When this channel is formed, the process already described for subsequent strokes takes place. If there are other charged centres, then further strokes may be started in the same way but all use the ionized channels of previous strokes. We can now see why there is a delay between the various strokes of a compound flash, namely while an ionized channel is being formed from the end of one stroke to the next centre of charge. We can also see why very large thunder clouds, which contain many centres of charge, are more likely to produce flashes with many individual strokes than small storms with, perhaps, only a single centre of charge. In the thunderstorms studied in England the different charged centres (e.g. A and B Fig. 5.1 (b)) are generally spaced out horizontally, but in South African storms the different charged centres seem to lie more nearly one above the other.

Those flashes which strike very high objects on the ground have a different structure to that described above. Lightning striking the Empire State Building, New York (some 400 m high), has been carefully studied. Here, in many cases the initial dart moves *upwards* from the top of the building to the

cloud and there is no bright return stroke, but instead a continuous current may flow down the ionized channel for several
tenths of a second.

When the thunder cloud is at a high level, many of the flashes
strike out into the clear air and no branch hits the ground.
Many flashes also take place within the cloud between the two
oppositely charged centres. Those flashes which never strike the
ground begin in the same way as flashes which do strike the
ground, i.e. with a relatively slow-moving intermittent dart, but
the second very bright stroke is absent.

F. *Radio Atmospherics*

Atmospherics produced by lightning flashes are caused partly
by the initial slow-moving dart of the first stroke of a flash and
partly by the very intense and rapid return stroke. The initial
darts of the second and subsequent strokes appear not to produce atmospherics since they move continuously and uniformly.
Those flashes which do not hit the ground produce atmospherics
only by their initial slow-moving dart, since they have no bright
return stroke. Owing to the slow movement of the original dart,
the atmospherics produced by it may be used to open the shutter
of a camera in time to photograph the flash. This technique has
been used when photographing lightning in the day-time when,
of course, it is not possible to leave the shutter open for a long
time as can de done at night.

4. THUNDER

Why does thunder rumble, crackle, or bang? The noise produced by lightning is due to the very sudden expansion of the air
in the path of a flash, when it is heated up to a high temperature
by the electrical discharge. The long-drawn-out thunder from a
single flash is due (except in mountainous country where echoes
can occur) to the slow speed with which sound travels through
the air—about 330 m/s at 0° C. When a flash is seen striking
the ground, as *DE* in Fig. 5.3, there is probably much branching
of the part of the discharge within the cloud as indicated in
the figure. If the flash were 10 km long from *A* to *G*, although
the whole flash was over in a small fraction of a second and the
noise was emitted almost at the same instant by all parts of the

flash, yet for a person standing at *O*, the sound of the thunder from the branch *G* will not be heard for about half a minute after that from branch *A*, and during this half-minute, sound will be heard continuously, coming from parts of the flash at greater and greater distances. A branch such as *AC*, which will probably carry only a small current, may be 300 m long and the sound from *C* will be heard at *O* about a second after that

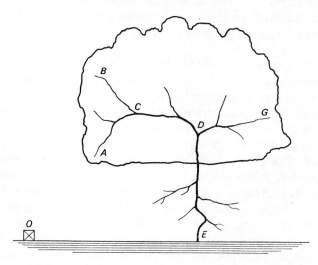

FIG. 5.3. Possible branching of lightning within a cloud indicating the way long-drawn-out thunder may be produced.

from *A* and during this time a continuous crackling noise will be heard as the sound from different parts of the branch arrives at *O*. On the other hand, a branch such as *BC* is nearly all at the same distance from *O*, so that the sound from all parts of this branch will arrive at *O* at the same time and produce a bang. In this way the sound from different parts of the flash will keep continually arriving at *O*, producing a series of crackles and bangs of varying intensity. The sound from the main part of the flash *DE*, which carries the maximum current, will all arrive at nearly the same time and produce a very loud bang, since all parts of this stroke are at nearly the same distance from *O*. Finally faint crackles will be heard from distant branches such as *DG*.

Distant thunder rumbles; only when the flash is near does it crack. This is the same for any distant sound, which always produces a rumbling noise. Sharp cracks involve sound waves of high frequency—short wavelengths—and these are rather rapidly absorbed or damped out in passing through the air, probably owing to irregularities of wind and temperature. The sounds consisting of low frequencies—rumbles—are less absorbed and so are heard to greater distances. In this connection it is of interest to note that although thunder is very loud when the flash is close, yet it is seldom heard at distances greater than about 20 km. Anyone can test this for themselves by measuring the time between the flash and the thunder from a distant storm which is not producing too frequent flashes to enable the thunder to be identified with the right flash. It is seldom that the time will be found to be greater than a minute.

5. THE ELECTRIC GENERATOR

The most fundamental, though the most difficult question posed by a thunderstorm is, 'How does the cloud become charged?' It is most disappointing to have to record that we still do not quite know for certain. There is no lack of theories but not a single one is yet generally accepted by all those who have studied thunderstorms most carefully. It would seem that the charging process takes place in two stages. (1) The larger drops of rain or the hail become negatively charged, while the surrounding cloud droplets and the air become positively charged. (2) The large negatively charged particles fall to the bottom of the cloud, while the positively charged cloud droplets and the air are carried up to the top of the cloud, thus separating the two charges. However, even this view is not without its difficulties, thus the largest drops of rain which reach the ground from a thunder cloud overhead are found to be positively charged. If these same large drops had carried negative charge downwards as they fell within the cloud, why is the sign of their charge reversed by the time that they reach the ground? One possibility is that as they fall through the air between the base of the cloud and the ground, they meet large numbers of positive ions streaming upwards in the strong electric field under the storm and their charge is neutralized and then reversed in sign by capture of positive ions. But if their charge is neutralized, or even reversed during this part of their fall, why does not a similar effect take place during their fall within the cloud? However, there are two differences in the conditions within the cloud and those below it. (i) Within the cloud, positive ions will be moving downwards, i.e. in the same direction as the falling drops, while below the cloud, the falling drops will be meeting the upward moving positive ions. (ii) The number of ions within the cloud will be very much less than in the clear air below the cloud, since within the cloud most of the ions will become attached to cloud droplets almost immediately after they are formed and so become relatively immobile. (Contrary to what might be expected at first sight, cloudy air is a worse conductor of electricity than clear air because of this immobilization of the ions). Further, there is often much 'brush' discharge from trees and other high points on the ground where the local electric potential gradient is exceptionally high and this brush discharge will greatly increase the number of ions.

The way in which the larger particles become negatively charged and the air and cloud droplets become positively charged is the main subject of discussion at the present time. There are many processes going on in a thunder cloud which are known to produce electrification, several of which involve the freezing of water or the interaction of water drops and ice crystals. The fact that the region which is most active in generating electricity is situated at a level where the temperature is a little below the freezing point, and where ice and water are likely to be mixed together, makes it probable that some of these processes are important in producing a thunderstorm. The following are some of the processes which are likely to occur in thunderstorms and which are known to produce electrification.

When water begins to freeze, the ice, and the water which remains unfrozen, acquire different electrical potentials; when a large wet hailstone falls rapidly through the air, some of the liquid water will be blown off it and this water will carry away a positive charge leaving the hailstone negatively charged.

When rime is deposited on a solid, the solid becomes electrically charged. Unfortunately different experimenters do not agree on the sign of the charge, but it is probable that it becomes negatively charged. (The processes mentioned above are found to depend very much on the purity of the water and small quantities of impurity may make large differences, even reversing the sign of the charge. This may account for some of the differences found by different experimenters.)

Ice crystals striking against one another in a cloud may become electrically charged.

The so-called 'influence' theories

This effect depends on the difference in the rate of capture of positive and negative ions by falling raindrops. If there is an initial positive electric field, the negative ions will be moving upwards through the air, while the positive ions will move downwards. Falling raindrops will capture more of the upward-moving negative ions than positive ions and hence will become negatively charged and will carry this charge down to the ground. We shall see that this effect may be of some importance, but it is unlikely to be the main source of electrification of a thunder cloud.

Breaking of water drops

When large water drops break up as they fall through the air, electrification takes place, the larger drops becoming positively charged and the small drops and the surrounding air become negatively charged. The electrification of the air near waterfalls by this process is well known. The main charges in a thunderstorm cannot be produced by this process since it would make the bottom of the cloud positive and the top negative, but it is thought that the breaking of water drops may be the cause of the small positive charge which is sometimes found near the bottom of a thunder cloud, below the main negative charge. Occasionally in warm climates thunderstorms have been observed whose tops do not reach the freezing level and in such cases it seems probable that the breaking of drops produces the main electrification, though the sign of the charges in such clouds has not yet been determined.

The theory of the generation of electricity in a thunderstorm which probably finds most favour at the present time is based on the following two facts.

(i) Ice contains both positive hydrogen ions (H^+) and negative hydroxyl ions (OH^-) and the number of these ions increases as temperature rises. (The total number of ions of each sign is, of course, the same.)

(ii) Hydrogen ions move much more freely through ice than hydroxyl ions do.

It follows from (i) and (ii) above that if a piece of ice is warmer at one end than at the other, then the warm end will contain more of both positive and negative ions than the cold end, but the positive ions from the warm end will diffuse quickly throughout the whole piece of ice, with the result that there will be an excess of positive ions in the cold part and a deficit in the warm part. In other words, the cold end will acquire a positive electric charge and the warm end a negative charge.

When we discussed the formation of rime (Chapter 4) we saw that when supercooled droplets of fog or cloud touch any piece of ice they immediately begin to freeze. If the droplets have a diameter of between 0·02 and 0·1 mm, then, when they freeze, an outer skin freezes first, leaving the inside still liquid. When the inside freezes later it will expand and burst the outer skin and splinters of ice will be thrown off. Now since the outside of the droplet is cooled by the cold air and the inside is warmed by the latent heat of freezing, the outside of the droplet will be colder than the inside. Consequently, as the result of the process we have described above, the outside of the droplet will be positively charged and any splinters of ice broken from it will carry away a positive charge, leaving the rest of the droplet negatively charged.

Observations of artificial formation of rime in the laboratory show that splinters are indeed thrown off and do carry away a positive charge. Now a hailstone falling through a cloud of supercooled water droplets will become covered by rime and consequently will acquire a negative electric charge, while the ice splinters thrown off into the surrounding air will carry a positive electric charge. The large hailstones, with their negative charge, will fall down through the rising air currents in the cloud, while the minute ice splinters, with their positive electric charge, will be carried upwards. It seems probable that this is the way in which the positive electric charge at the top of a thunder cloud and the negative charge near the bottom are produced. Although the electric charge on a single splinter of ice is very small, measurements made in the laboratory during the formation of rime indicate that the rate of formation of the electric charges in a thunderstorm could be accounted for in this way. The above theory is new and may well have to be modified in detail in the future, but there seem to be very good reasons for thinking that the production of electricity in a thunderstorm is in some way associated with the freezing of water drops.

6. ATMOSPHERIC ELECTRICITY IN FINE WEATHER

A. *The Air to Earth Current*

It has been known for a long time that there is a large electrical potential gradient in the atmosphere in fine weather. Thus the electrical potential of the air at a height of 2 m above the ground in the open, away from trees or buildings, is about 500 V above that of the ground. However, the air is an exceedingly bad conductor of electricity and even this large electric force results in only a very small current flowing from the atmosphere to the ground—about a millionth of an ampere per square kilometre of the earth's surface—but this adds up to between 1000 and 2000 A flowing into the whole earth. Naturally this raises the question, where does this current come from, and where is the return current, for clearly the earth is not being charged up continuously? The current flowing into the earth can easily be measured by exposing a large metal plate, mounted on very good insulators, at ground level. The plate is connected to an electrometer and as the current flows into it, the electrometer will indicate an increase of potential. (In practice certain precautions have to be taken to allow for the minute-to-minute changes in the general electric field.) The electric field can also easily be measured by fixing a burning fuse on a very good insulator at a height of a metre or two above the ground and connecting it to an electrometer which will indicate the potential of the air at the position of the burning fuse. The function of the burning fuse is to provide large numbers of ions, and other types of collectors may be used, such as radio-active collectors, which also ionize the air near them.

B. *Conductivity of the Air*

Ions and ionization

Natural atmospheric air is always a slight conductor of electricity owing to its slight ionization and we may now stop for a moment to consider how an electric current flows through a gas. In Chapter 1, section 9 we discussed briefly the nature of atoms and molecules. These contain both positive and negative electric charges but, since their numbers are equal, the atom or molecule as a whole is uncharged, and when all the atoms or molecules of a gas are in this condition the gas is an insulator and will not conduct electricity. However, it may happen that an electron has been knocked off an atom or molecule, when the atom or molecule will have one excess positive charge; the atom or molecule is then called an ion and is said to be ionized. On the other hand, an electron that has been knocked off an atom may become attached to a neutral atom or molecule, giving it an excess negative charge, and it then becomes a negative ion.

In the lower atmosphere an electron that is knocked off an atom very rapidly becomes attached to another atom or molecule, but in the highest atmosphere, where the mean free path of molecules and electrons is very long, free electrons may exist for a considerable time and, as the electrons move much more rapidly than ions, they are mainly responsible for the conductivity of the ionosphere that will be described in Chapter 8. If an ionized gas at normal pressure is placed between two metal plates, one charged positively and the other negatively, the positive ions will be attracted to the negative plate and vice versa. Although the ions will be continually colliding with other molecules and changing their direction of motion after each impact, yet there will always be a constant tendency for them to drift towards the charged plates. This motion of the ions through the gas constitutes an electric current and this is the way electric currents flow through a gas. The ionization of gases is usually caused by collisions with other fast-moving atoms, molecules, or electrons (e.g. as in cosmic rays), but can also be caused by the absorption of ultra-violet light, X-rays, or 'gamma' rays from radioactive materials.

The ionization of the air near the ground is produced partly by radioactive materials in the ground and in the lower air and partly by cosmic radiation coming in from outer space, but that produced by radioactivity is much greater than that caused by cosmic radiation. However, the amount of radioactive matter in the air rapidly decreases with increasing height, while the intensity of the down-coming, cosmic radiation increases with height. As a result, after a small decrease at first, the ionization —and therefore the electrical conductivity of the air—increases with increasing height and the air in the stratosphere is a much better conductor than the air near the ground, though it is still a very poor conductor in comparison with the air in the ionosphere, where the ionization is caused by very short-wave solar radiation. Although the conductivity of the air changes so much with height, the electric current flowing downwards through the air is nearly the same at all levels below the ionosphere.

c. *Cosmic Radiation*

It is outside the scope of this book to give any detailed account of cosmic radiation, but since it plays so important a part in ionizing the air, the following brief notes may be of interest.

Cosmic radiation was first discovered during a study of the ionization of the atmosphere. It was found that even in a closed vessel, shielded as carefully as possible from the influence of radioactive material, the air was continually being ionized whereas, had there been no other source of ionization, the ions should have quickly recombined, leaving the air a good insulator. Moreover, it was found that if such a vessel was taken up on a balloon into the upper troposphere, then the ionization inside it increased considerably. This indicated that the ionization was caused by a very penetrating radiation coming down from above.

As a result of a great deal of research work, we now know that the outside of the atmosphere is continuously being bombarded by extremely high-speed particles; about one of these particles falls on each square centimetre of the outer atmosphere per second and the total energy received by the earth in this type of radiation is about equal to that in starlight. The bombarding particles are free electrons and atomic nuclei, the nuclei being completely stripped of all their electrons. Hydrogen atoms are by far the most numerous, although there are some atoms of helium and a very few of the other elements.

The energies of these incoming particles varies over a very wide range but some have an exceedingly high energy—far exceeding anything that can be produced by the largest artificial particle accelerators. These particles arrive at the earth in all directions from space, though the slower of them may be deflected by the earth's magnetic field shortly before they reach the earth. At the time of a very intense solar flare, particles similar to the slowest in cosmic rays are shot out from the sun. The origin of the major part—the cosmic part—is still largely unknown.

When these high-speed particles enter the upper atmosphere they strike the atoms in the air, with the result that entirely new particles, known as mesons, are produced together with neutrons. These mesons have a mass intermediate between that of an electron and that of a hydrogen atom and have very short lives. The primary particles of cosmic radiation do not penetrate to a level much below 15 km above the ground, but the mesons penetrate right down to the ground and even well into the ground. These particles cause the ionization of the air in the troposphere, including that in a closed vessel, by which cosmic radiation was first discovered. When an exceptionally high-speed particle strikes an atom in the upper air an even more remarkable phenomenon occurs, known as a shower, when some millions of secondary particles are formed and these may strike the ground simultaneously over an area a few hundred metres across. The air in the ionosphere is too rare to stop many cosmic particles, with the result that they cause little ionization at this great height.

While cosmic radiation is of great interest as the cause of the ionization in the lower atmosphere, by far its greatest interest is due to the fact that these exceptionally high-speed particles have proved an invaluable tool in investigating the structure of the atomic nucleus and in the discovery of a whole series of unstable particles such as the mesons.

D. *The Origin of the Fine Weather Atmospheric Electric Current*

Earlier in this chapter it was shown that the tops of thunder clouds, which may reach up to the tropopause, are positively charged. Owing to the relatively good electrical conductivity of the air in the stratosphere, this positive charge can flow up to the ionosphere—or perhaps we should say the negative charge can flow down from the ionosphere into the top of the thunder cloud. In this way the ionosphere becomes charged up positively and owing to the very good electrical conductivity of the ionosphere, the charge quickly spreads through it and the ionosphere over the whole world becomes positively charged to about half a million volts relatively to the earth. The earth and the ionosphere can thus be regarded as two concentric conducting spheres separated by a rather poor insulator, viz. the air. Thunderstorms are continuously charging the ionosphere positively and this charge is continuously leaking back to the earth through the air in all parts of the world. The negative charge in thunderstorms flows to the ground partly in the lightning flashes, partly in small continuous discharges between two bright strokes and partly in the strong conduction current through the air underneath thunderstorms, where there may be a strong enough electric potential gradient to cause brush discharges from trees, etc. on the ground. Actual measurements of the electric current flowing into the ground under thunderstorms show that there is a current of about one ampere per storm, and as it has been estimated that there are about 2000 thunderstorms in existence all over the world at any one time, it is seen that thunderstorms will account for the fine weather electric current. If thunderstorms were not continuously charging up the ionosphere, the leakage current to earth would discharge it in a few minutes.

The discovery of the origin of the fine weather electric current which flows down through the air also explains a curious diurnal variation of the electric potential gradient in the atmosphere. In industrial districts the potential gradient as measured near the ground is much affected by local pollution in the air, but over the oceans and other regions where the air is unpolluted, it is found that the potential gradient is a maximum, about 7 p.m. and a minimum about 4 a.m. G.M.T. and the variation is about 15 per cent above and below the mean value. This is a world-wide phenomenon and the maximum and minimum values occur at the same universal time all over the world, i.e. at the same instants regardless of local time. Now thunderstorms take place mostly over land areas in low latitudes and mostly in the afternoon, when the lower air is strongly heated by the sun. A careful estimate of the number of thunderstorms in progress at each hour in all parts of the world shows that they reach a maximum between 2 p.m. and 7 p.m. G.M.T. while on account of the relatively few thunderstorms in the Pacific Ocean, there is a minimum about 4 a.m. G.M.T. These times are in reasonably good agreement with the times of the maximum and minimum of the electrical potential gradient.

6. Ozone in the Atmosphere

I. INTRODUCTION

As was briefly mentioned in Chapter 1, although there is very little ozone in the atmosphere, it is of interest for three quite different reasons. First, since ozone absorbs ultra-violet light very strongly, a large part of the ultra-violet radiation from the sun (about 5 per cent of the total energy received by the earth from the sun) is absorbed by the ozone high in the atmosphere, and this energy heats the air at this height and is the cause of the warm region at a height of about 50 km above the ground. Second, the amount of ozone in the atmosphere above any place is found to vary considerably from day to day and, although most of the ozone is situated above the tropopause, yet these variations are found to be closely associated with variations in the weather. Finally, in addition to the day-to-day variations, the ozone has a very unexpected type of annual variation, and its distribution over the world is equally unexpected. From these variations with season and latitude, it has been possible to deduce something about the general world-wide circulation of the air between the troposphere and the stratosphere, and this has recently become of special interest in view of the fall-out of radioactive matter from nuclear explosions.

2. GENERAL CHARACTERISTICS OF OZONE

There are three different forms of oxygen in the atmosphere and for the benefit of the reader who has but little knowledge of chemistry we may distinguish between them as follows.

Oxygen atoms

In this, the simplest form of oxygen, the atoms exist as separate units. Much of the oxygen in the highest atmosphere exists in this form.

Oxygen molecules

In this form each molecule contains two atoms of oxygen which are bound together. This is the normal form in which oxygen exists in the lower atmosphere. If separate oxygen atoms existed in the lower atmosphere, they would very rapidly combine in pairs to form oxygen molecules.

Ozone

Each molecule of ozone contains three atoms of oxygen.

A. *Chemical Properties of Ozone*

While ozone is a form of oxygen, its properties are very different from those of normal oxygen. One of its three atoms is easily given up to any substance with which it comes into contact and which is readily oxidizable, and the ozone is thereby destroyed. A large amount of energy is required to form ozone from oxygen and this energy is given up again when ozone returns to normal oxygen; pure ozone is actually explosive and will detonate under suitable conditions. On the other hand, a large amount of energy is required to dissociate a molecule of oxygen into two single atoms of oxygen and this energy is released again when two atoms of oxygen recombine to form a molecule of oxygen.

B. *Physical Properties*

For our present purpose the chemical properties of ozone are of less importance than its physical properties, the most important of which is its ability to absorb radiation in certain parts of the spectrum. Oxygen is almost transparent to the whole of the visible, infra-red, and ultra-violet parts of the spectrum, absorbing only the rather short wavelengths, less than 2400 Å. On the other hand, ozone absorbs radiation in three different parts of the spectrum. (*a*) It absorbs very strongly in the ultra-violet region between about 3300 and 2200 Å, the strongest absorption being at a wavelength of about 2500 Å where it is extremely intense. The small amount of ozone in the upper atmosphere effectively cuts off the whole of the in-coming radiation from the sun of wavelengths less than 3000 Å. It is this absorption of solar radiation that is the cause of the formation of the warm region in the atmosphere at a height of about 50 km that was described in Chapter 3 (see Fig. 3.6). It is also of interest to note that, if it were not for this absorption, the inhabitants of the earth would be subject to excessive sunburn. (*b*) Ozone absorbs radiation in the yellow-green region of the spectrum. Though the absorption here is rather weak, yet, because it occurs in a part of the spectrum where the amount of in-coming solar radiation is at its maximum intensity, it gives rise to appreciable warming in the upper atmosphere. (*c*) The third important region of absorption by ozone is in the infra-red part of the spectrum, chiefly at wavelengths around 9·5 μm (95 000 Å). This absorption band of ozone happens to come in a part of the spectrum where the out-going radiation from the earth and the lower atmosphere is at its maximum. It has been suggested that the absorption of this out-going terrestrial radiation leads to some warming of the stratosphere, but the theoretical treatment of the subject is very difficult and it is still uncertain whether this warming is important or not.

c. *Formation and Destruction of Ozone*

When the oxygen in the upper atmosphere absorbs solar radiation of wavelengths shorter than about 2400 Å, molecules of oxygen are broken up into atoms of oxygen. When one of these atoms of oxygen encounters another molecule of oxygen it may combine with it to form a molecule of ozone. It is believed that almost all the ozone in the atmosphere is formed in this way. The rate at which ozone is formed in the upper atmosphere will naturally be greatest at the levels where there are plenty of both oxygen atoms and oxygen molecules and the main region of formation is at heights above 30 km. There is, however, another process going on at the same time; when ozone absorbs solar radiation of wavelengths around 2500 Å, it is itself destroyed, forming a molecule of oxygen and an atom of oxygen. However, the free atom of oxygen may recombine with another molecule of oxygen to form ozone again. On the other hand, an atom of oxygen may meet a molecule of ozone, in which case they will form two molecules of oxygen, thus destroying the ozone. In this 'photo-chemical' region of the upper atmosphere these processes of formation and decomposition go on at the same time and there will finally be an equilibrium between the amount of ozone being formed and the amount being destroyed. Any ozone which may be carried down to the ground is immediately destroyed by contact with smoke and with vegetation. In the photo-chemical region there may be as much as one part of ozone by volume to every 100 000 parts of air. The ozone in the photo-chemical region will be slowly mixed with all the rest of the atmosphere and if there was no destruction of ozone near the ground, the whole atmosphere would contain something like this proportion of ozone, an amount that would be extremely unpleasant to breathe. While, therefore, the ozone is useful in cutting off injurious ultra-violet sunlight, it is fortunate that it is so rapidly destroyed at the ground! Because the ozone is destroyed at the ground there is a gradual drift of ozone from the photo-chemical region downwards through the whole of the lower atmosphere. Any ozone which comes below a height of about 20 km will be protected from the sun's ultra-violet light by the ozone above it and will have a life of several months, provided that it does not come near the ground. Measurements made during the daytime above a grass field have shown that there is a very rapid decrease in the ozone concentration as the surface is approached, and among the grass blades there is a negligible amount of ozone. On a still night, when there is little turbulence in the lower air, the downward transport of ozone is greatly reduced and then all the air for many metres above the ground may be almost free from ozone. In smoky air it is generally impossible to detect any ozone. (The ozone which is said to be formed by sunlight on the 'smog' of Los Angeles is a peculiar case and not yet thoroughly understood.)

Ozone may be formed not only by the action of ultra-violet light but also by the action of a high-voltage electric discharge —indeed this is the way that ozone is generally produced in artificial ozonizers. We may thus expect that ozone will be formed in thunderstorms, and observations indicate that this is probably the case, though the observations are difficult and somewhat uncertain. However, the ozone produced by thunderstorms is certainly a very small part of the whole ozone in the atmosphere and is, at most, of only local importance.

3. MEASUREMENT OF THE AMOUNT OF OZONE IN THE ATMOSPHERE

When studying the ozone in the atmosphere we generally wish to measure one of two things: (*a*) the total amount of ozone in the air above any particular place, i.e. in the whole column of air from the ground to the top of the atmosphere; (*b*) the concentration of the ozone in the air at any particular place, e.g. the concentration in the air at ground level or in the air around a balloon as it ascends through the atmosphere (from which we get the vertical distribution of ozone in the air).

A. *Total Amount of Ozone—Optical Method*

The total amount of ozone in the air above any place is most conveniently and accurately measured by observing how much certain wavelengths in sunlight are absorbed in their passage through the atmosphere. For this purpose it is usual to measure the intensity of some wavelength near the long-wave edge of the strong absorption band of ozone in the ultra-violet region. The wavelength used must be carefully chosen since, if it is too long, the absorption by ozone will be too small to give accurate values of the ozone, while if it is too short the absorption may be so strong that the light which reaches the ground may be too weak to measure accurately. In practice wavelengths around 3050 to 3100 Å are generally used. The solar energy in these wavelengths is reduced to about a tenth in its passage through the atmosphere, the actual amount varying with the height of the sun and the amount of ozone present. Additional observations are made to find what would be the intensity of the light if there were no ozone present. It would be possible to use only one wavelength in the solar spectrum for these measurements but there are great advantages in measuring the *ratio* of the intensities of two adjacent wavelengths such as 3050 and 3250 Å, the first being strongly absorbed by ozone while the second is but little absorbed. In such a case we get nearly the full effect of the absorption at 3050 Å while the instrumental measurements are much easier and some troublesome effects, such as the scattering of light by the air and by haze, are nearly eliminated (see Fig. 6.1).

Since the absorption increases very rapidly as the wavelength

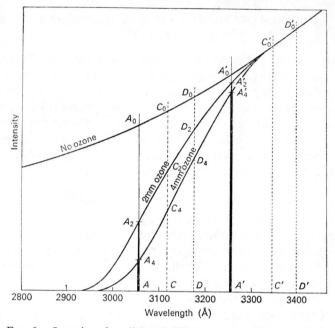

FIG. 6.1. Intensity of sunlight of different wavelengths reaching the ground.

The curve A_0, A_0', D_0' shows the intensity of each wavelength which would reach the ground with the sun overhead if there was no ozone in the atmosphere. The curve $A_2 A_2'$ shows the intensity at ground level if there was 2 mm of ozone in the atmosphere, while the curve $A_4 A_4'$ allows for 4 mm of ozone in the atmosphere. Only the *ratio* of two wavelengths, e.g. $A_2 A/A_2' A'$, is measured, not their individual intensities. Note that each additional 2 mm of ozone approximately halves the intensity of wavelength A reaching the ground, while the intensity of A' is hardly affected. Other pairs of wavelengths such as C and C', or D' and D, may be used.

decreases it is necessary to isolate the exact wavelengths required and some form of spectrograph, i.e. monochromator, must be used for accurate work. Further, the intensity of sunlight at these short wavelengths is extremely weak compared with the intensity of the visible parts of the spectrum, and great precautions must be taken in the design of the instrument to prevent the very much stronger light of longer wavelengths from producing serious errors due to scattering by all the optical surfaces in the instrument. The intensities of the required wavelengths may be measured either by photographic or photoelectric methods. In the first case the spectrum of sunlight is photographed and the ratio of the intensities of the wavelengths used is deduced from the density of their photographic images. When the photo-electric method is used the required wavelengths are isolated by two slits in the monochromator and their intensities are measured by photo-electric cells behind the slits, suitable electronic amplification being used. The amount of ozone in the atmosphere can be measured by these methods with an error of not more than 2 or 3 per cent. The instrument is always used with direct sunlight when this is possible, but when sunlight cannot be used because of clouds, measurements may be made on the light from the clear zenith sky or even from the cloudy sky, though with somewhat less accuracy.

B. Concentration of Ozone—Chemical Methods

(i) Potassium iodide method

When it is desired to measure the concentration of ozone in the air, i.e. the amount of ozone in any given volume of air, a chemical method is most frequently employed, usually the reaction in which ozone liberates iodine from a solution of potassium iodide, the amount of iodine liberated being proportional to the amount of ozone passed through the solution. Various well-known methods may be used for estimating the amount of liberated iodine.

(ii) Chemi-luminescent method

Another method that has been recently introduced makes use of the fact that if air containing ozone is passed over certain luminescent materials they give out light and the amount of light is proportional to the amount of ozone in the air passed through the apparatus. The light is measured by photo-electric methods.

C. Vertical Distribution of Ozone

(i) Chemical methods

The most valuable use of chemical methods is in the determination of the vertical distribution of the ozone in the atmosphere, using apparatus sent up on a balloon. This apparatus gives the concentration of ozone in the air at the different heights as it ascends and descends. If the potassium iodide method is used, the instrument is designed to produce an electric current that is proportional to the amount of iodine being released. This current controls a radio transmitter whose signals are received on the ground so that the ozone concentration at the height of the balloon can be recorded. If the chemi-luminescent method is used, the light is measured by a photocell and the current from the photocell is telemetered down to the ground as before. These chemical methods are now producing very valuable information.

(ii) *Optical methods using balloons or rockets*

The vertical distribution of ozone in the atmosphere may be measured by sending up a spectrograph on a balloon or rocket and recording the solar spectrum. The instrument will measure the total amount of ozone above it at any height, just as in the case of spectrographic instruments used on the ground that we described previously. As the instrument ascends, the amount of ozone above it will decrease, and the rate of decrease will be particularly rapid when it is ascending through regions that contain much ozone. In this method photographs are sometimes taken of the solar spectrum that are measured when the instrument comes down to earth again. More usually the intensity of the required wavelengths in the solar spectrum is measured by photo-electric instruments carried on the balloon and the results transmitted by radio to the ground. The amount of ozone at any given height is calculated from the rate of decrease in the total amount of ozone above the instrument as it ascends. When the instrument is carried on a rocket, the method gives accurate results for the vertical distribution of ozone in the highest layers of the atmosphere. It is not very accurate for the lower levels where there is always much ozone above the instrument and this amount is only slowly decreasing with height. In some cases optical filters have been used to isolate the required regions of the spectrum, but such instruments, though cheaper, are not so accurate as spectroscopic instruments.

(iii) *The Götz method*

Yet another method of measuring the vertical distribution of ozone in the atmosphere is to make measurements with a spectroscopic instrument on the ground in the same way as we described for measuring the total ozone, but to use the light from the clear blue zenith sky and to continue the measurements from noon to sunset (or from sunrise to noon). In the region of the spectrum with which we are now concerned, i.e. between 3000 and 3500 Å, the sunlight passing through the air will be scattered—without appreciable absorption—by the main gases in the atmosphere, nitrogen and oxygen, while it will be absorbed by ozone. The proportion of light scattered by a given volume of air will be governed by the density of the air and will therefore depend on the height of the volume considered, and all wavelengths in this part of the spectrum will be scattered in roughly the same proportion. On the other hand, the absorption of light by the ozone in a given volume of air will depend on the concentration of ozone in the air and on the wavelength of the light. The light which is received at ground level from the clear blue zenith sky is, of course, sunlight which has been scattered by the air. Sunlight illuminates the whole depth of the atmosphere and light scattered by the air at all heights contributes to the zenith skylight which reaches the instrument. Sunlight, on entering the atmosphere, first passes on a sloping path through the upper atmosphere down to the level at which it is scattered, and then that part that reaches the instrument passes on a vertical path down to the ground. Some of the sunlight will be scattered by the air above the main ozone region, some within it, and some below it. The amount of sunlight that is scattered at any given height will depend primarily on two things: (i) the amount of air available to scatter light at that height; (ii) the intensity of light reaching the height of scattering after absorption by ozone on the long sloping path down to the level where it is scattered. The amount of light that is scattered below the ozone region will rapidly decrease as the sun sets owing to the increasing length of its path through the ozone region. On the other hand, light that is scattered above the ozone region will be much the same whether the sun is high or low, since there is no absorption by ozone before it is scattered and it always passes through the ozone region on the short vertical path. During the time when the sun is setting, changes in the spectroscopic character of the skylight that reaches the instrument will depend on the vertical distribution of the ozone in the atmosphere, so that measurements made on the zenith skylight during this period allow us to calculate the vertical distribution of the ozone.

This Götz method is very useful in so far as measurements are easily made from the ground (given clear skies), but the necessary calculation is difficult and much less detail is obtained about the vertical distribution than with the chemical method. Thus it could never show the sudden increase in ozone concentration just above the tropopause that is often shown by the chemical method. It does, however, give an accurate value for the average height of the total ozone in the atmosphere.

(iv) *The eclipse method*

An artificial earth satellite, when travelling round the earth, will frequently pass into, and out of, the earth's shadow. At such times it will be illuminated by sunlight that has passed nearly horizontally through the upper layers of the earth's atmosphere and that has suffered strong absorption by the ozone in these high layers. The spectrum of the sunlight received by the satellite may be measured, either by an instrument carried on the satellite, or the light reflected from the satellite may be measured from the ground. From such measurements it is possible to deduce the amount of ozone at different heights in the upper atmosphere. Measurements of a similar kind may be made when there is a partial eclipse of the moon, since the part of the moon on the edge of the earth's shadow will also be illuminated by sunlight which has passed through the upper regions of the earth's atmosphere.

(v) *Infra-red method*

Ozone strongly absorbs infra-red radiation of a wavelength about $9.5\ \mu m$ ($95\ 000$ Å), and the intensity of this absorption depends not only on the amount of ozone present but also on the total atmospheric pressure at the level at which the ozone exists. Any given amount of ozone will thus absorb differently according to the height in the atmosphere (and therefore the pressure) at which it is. Hence there is clearly a possibility of deducing the height of the ozone in the atmosphere if we measure both the total amount of ozone by the ultra-violet method and also the absorption of sunlight in the infra-red region. Measurements can also be made of the emission of $9.5\ \mu m$ radiation by the ozone in the atmosphere. Such measurements allow an estimate of the vertical distribution of the ozone in the troposphere to be made, but unfortunately the results are not very accurate for the higher levels.

4. DISTRIBUTION OF OZONE OVER THE WORLD AT DIFFERENT SEASONS

A. *Total Ozone*

We now come to consider the results of the many thousands of measurements of atmospheric ozone that have been made all over the world. It will be convenient to give first a general, world-wide picture and then go on to the changes in the amount of ozone that occur from day to day and from place to place, and are found to be closely related to changes in the weather conditions. Fig. 6.2 gives the annual variation of the total ozone† for each 10° of latitude in the northern hemisphere. This diagram is based on observations made at twenty-four places, mainly during the International Geophysical Year, and represents average conditions for all longitudes, any abnormalities being averaged out. The results of the same observations are presented again in another manner in Fig. 6.3 where lines of equal ozone are plotted on a diagram with latitude as ordinates (vertically) and the month of the year as abscissae (horizontally). Unfortunately observations have not yet been made at enough places in the southern hemisphere to allow a similar diagram to be drawn accurately for that hemisphere, though observations near the South Pole show a most interesting abnormality in that region.

Fig. 6.2 shows that all places with a latitude greater than 40° N. have a large seasonal variation in the total ozone. Since the ozone is formed by sunlight, it might be expected that at these latitudes the maximum amount would be found in the late summer and the minimum in the late winter, just as the maximum and minimum of temperature are found at these seasons. However, this is far from being the case, the maximum

---

† It is usual to express the total amount of ozone in the atmosphere above any one place as the thickness of the same amount of ozone if it was all condensed into a layer of pure ozone at the surface of the earth, i.e. at normal temperature and pressure.

actually being in March or April and the minimum about October. The reason for this will be discussed later. The highest ozone values of all are found in the Arctic regions during the spring, and it is important to note that even in high latitudes the amount of ozone begins to increase during December and

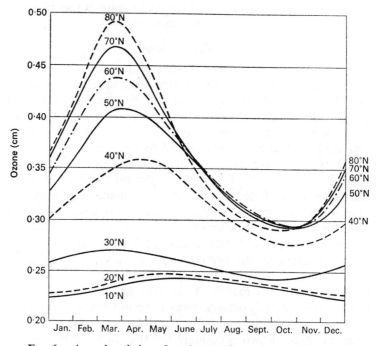

FIG. 6.2. Annual variation of total ozone for each 10° of N. latitude.

January when the sun is very low even at midday or may actually be below the horizon. It is also interesting to see that during the months of August to November all places with a latitude greater than about 45° N. have almost the same amount of ozone, so that at this season of the year there is hardly any variation of total ozone with latitude; this is an important point to remember when we come to consider how the day-to-day variations of ozone are produced. There is a very rapid decrease in the amount of ozone between latitudes 40 and 30° N., particularly in the spring. This is shown in Fig. 6.3 by the crowding together of the lines of equal ozone in these latitudes. South of

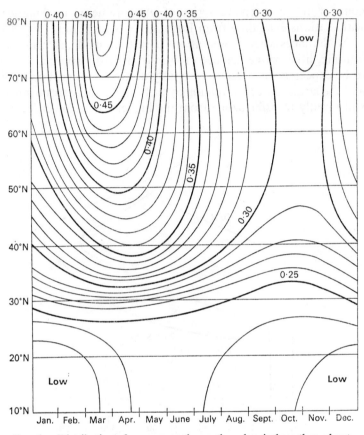

FIG. 6.3. Distribution of ozone over the northern hemisphere throughout the year.

about 25° N. there seems to be little change of ozone with latitude or with season. It is rather surprising that the tropical belt of low ozone shows little sign of moving north and south with the sun, being in much the same place in both December and June.

B. *Vertical Distribution of Ozone in Different Parts of the World*

Great progress has recently been made in measuring the vertical distribution of ozone in different parts of the world. While the earliest measurements were made in Europe, as has so often happened in other cases, most of our knowledge has come from an extensive series of measurements in America, with stations extending from Bolivia (16° S.) to Thule (76° N.). At all places where observations have been made, at whatever latitude, little ozone has been found in the troposphere. This is to be expected since ozone is rapidly destroyed at ground level, and the large amount of mixing by turbulence in the troposphere will rapidly transfer ozone from the higher to the lower levels.

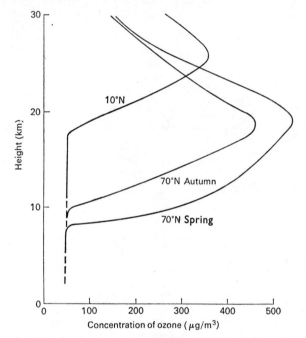

FIG. 6.4. The diagram shows the average vertical distribution of ozone during the spring and autumn in high latitudes and at all seasons in low latitudes. The rate of decrease of ozone with height above about 30 km is such that the ratio of ozone to air is roughly constant.

In very low latitudes the vertical distribution of ozone is fairly simple and shows little change from day to day and throughout the year. The tropopause here is, of course, always high (about 17 km) and is generally well defined by a sudden increase in temperature. On entering the stratosphere the ozone immediately begins to rise and a regular and steady increase continues up to a maximum at a height of about 25 to 27 km. Between the tropopause and the maximum, the concentration of ozone increases more than ten times while, owing to the decrease in the density of the air with height, the ozone/air ratio increases more than 100 times. Above about 25 to 27 km the concentration of ozone begins to decrease at much the same rate as the density of the air decreases, so that the ozone/air ratio remains nearly constant up to the greatest heights reached by balloons (about 35 km).

Measurements made in the stratosphere at higher latitudes show a more complicated structure. The level at which the maximum concentration of ozone occurs is much lower near the poles than near the equator, and shows a steady fall with latitude similar to the fall in the height of the tropopause, being only about 18 km at Thule (76° N.) and at Halley Bay (75° S.). Although there is always a general increase in the concentration of ozone with increasing height in the lower stratosphere, there are sometimes large irregularities, and layers of low ozone may be found above layers of higher ozone. In some cases, layers a few kilometres thick are found in which even the ozone/air ratio is less than in a lower layer.

The changes in the vertical distribution with season are very similar at all places outside the tropics. The maximum in the total ozone that is always found in spring is produced by a general increase in the concentration of ozone between the tropopause and about 20 to 25 km, with a corresponding decrease in the autumn. At high levels, above 30 km, where photochemical formation takes place, the maximum is in summer rather than in the spring, as one might expect. However, the amount of ozone at these high levels is small and the annual variation in the total ozone is mainly governed by the amount of ozone between the tropopause and 25 km.

The large variations of ozone with height that are sometimes found in the lower stratosphere, in middle and high latitudes, were unexpected, and their cause is still not well understood. They are, however, of much interest and we will therefore consider them a little more fully. As we have seen, the ozone below about 25 km is very stable, being protected from solar radiation by the ozone above it. Variations of the ozone concentration with height might be caused in one of three ways or a combination of them all.

(1) Diffusion due to turbulence will always transfer ozone

from regions of high ozone/air ratio to regions of low ozone/air ratio. If there is much turbulence in any layer, the ozone/air ratio will be nearly uniform throughout the layer; conversely if there is little turbulence there may be a large difference in the ozone/air ratio between the top and the bottom of the layer. The amount of turbulence in any layer depends very largely on the fall of temperature within the layer, and we should expect to find that layers in which the temperature falls rapidly with height would be regions of high turbulence, and therefore the ozone/air ratio would increase only slowly with height (e.g. the troposphere). On the other hand, layers in which the temperature changes only little with height or even increases with height, would be layers of little turbulence and might show a large difference in the ozone/air ratio between the top and the bottom.

(2) If the air is generally subsiding over a region it will bring down air having a high ozone/air ratio, while a general rising current will carry up air which is weak in ozone. If there is also some spreading sideways, this may cause a layer weak in ozone to be found above one rich in ozone.

(3) There may be cases in which tongues of air rich or weak in ozone are carried horizontally between other layers. Thus if air from the upper tropical troposphere were carried polewards into the stratosphere of higher latitudes, it would result in a layer of low ozone being sandwiched between layers of higher ozone.

Occasionally tongues of stratospheric air are drawn down into the troposphere. These cases are usually associated with polar fronts or discontinuities in the tropopause. This stratospheric air is both drier and richer in ozone than the normal tropospheric air.

c. *Cause of the Variation of Ozone with Season and Latitude*

We must now consider why the ozone in the atmosphere has this curious distribution which we have just described and why it changes in so peculiar a manner from season to season. Since the ozone is formed from oxygen by the photo-chemical action of sunlight at a height of some 30 km or more, the amount of ozone in this photo-chemical region may be expected to be greatest at those times and places where the sunlight is most intense, i.e. over the equator and also in high latitudes in summer. From this photo-chemical region, the ozone will be carried down by small-scale turbulence, but as the turbulence in the stratosphere is weak, owing to its very stable structure, the transport through the stratosphere will be slow. When the ozone reaches the tropopause it will be caught up in the much stronger turbulence of the troposphere and will be rapidly mixed throughout that region. The amount of ozone in the photo-chemical region is only about a quarter of the total ozone in the atmosphere, and the greater part of the ozone is shielded from the active wavelengths of sunlight by the ozone above it and will have a life of some months at least, though any ozone reaching the ground will be rapidly destroyed on contact with vegetation or smoke.

If there were no large-scale movements of air, the ozone distribution over the world might be expected to be similar to that in the photo-chemical region, but clearly this is not the case, e.g. we find the maximum amount of ozone in high latitudes in spring when, on photo-chemical grounds, we should expect it to be nearly at a minimum. Any large-scale up or down movements of the air will hinder or help the downward drift of ozone, while large-scale wind currents will transport ozone horizontally to different parts of the world. When looking for the cause of the very dry air in the stratosphere (Chapter 2) we had to suppose that there was a general, slow, rising current of air from the upper troposphere into the stratosphere in very low latitudes. Such a belt of rising air would also account very well for the low value of the total ozone near the equator.

Air passing upwards from the troposphere into the stratosphere in low latitudes must return to the troposphere somewhere and it is thought that this return takes place mainly in high latitudes in winter, and that a given mass of air remains in the stratosphere for a time of the order of 6 months before it returns to the troposphere. The descent of air in high latitudes in winter is probably aided by the fact that the air at heights of 15 to 40 km at this season is very cold and therefore heavy (see Fig. 2.2). There is probably also some return of air from the stratosphere to the troposphere in cyclonic areas of middle latitudes; it will be remembered that the upper troposphere is very dry in these regions, indicating that the air has descended from the stratosphere.

On entering the equatorial stratosphere the tropospheric air will spread out towards higher latitudes. The descending air at great heights over the winter pole will cause air to flow in from lower latitudes to take its place, and if this movement extends up to the photo-chemical region, ozone-rich air will be carried polewards, and as it descends it will fill the polar stratosphere with ozone-rich air. Since the tropopause here is low there is relatively much air in the stratosphere, and as this air is rich in ozone the total ozone will be high, agreeing with observation. Observations of the vertical distribution of ozone agree well with these suggestions; the ozone concentration at a height of 25 to 35 km shows an annual variation with a maximum in the summer and a minimum in the winter, while the ozone concentration in the lower layers of the stratosphere shows a maximum in the spring and a minimum in the autumn, in agreement with the total ozone.

The concentration of ozone (i.e. ozone per unit volume) is, on the average, nearly constant at all heights throughout the troposphere. Since the ozone is being transported downwards by turbulence, it might be expected that its concentration would be greater at high levels than lower down. The *ratio* of ozone to air *is* greater in the upper troposphere than below, but since the air is compressed at lower levels by the greater atmospheric pressure, there is more of both air and ozone in a given volume at low levels and this may balance the smaller ozone/air ratio. Thus the amount of ozone in a given volume may be much the same at all heights within the troposphere.

D. *Anomalies in the General World-wide Pattern*

As already described, the ozone in nearly all parts of the world shows a marked seasonal variation with maximum in the spring and minimum in the autumn, the range (maximum minus minimum) increasing from zero at the equator, until near the North Pole the spring value is nearly twice that in the autumn. Apart from day-to-day changes, which are associated with changing meteorological conditions, the annual curve has a fairly smooth wave-form with a tendency to show a steep rise in the spring. There are two major departures from this regular world-wide pattern.

(1) Observations made at Halley Bay in the Weddell Sea

(latitude 75° S.), during and since the International Geophysical Year, show that the total ozone there has the usual low value in the autumn, but it does not rise much during the winter, nor even during the spring; then in November—well after the time of the expected spring maximum for the southern hemisphere— the ozone suddenly rises and within a week or two reaches normal values (i.e. values equal to those found at a corresponding season and latitude in the northern hemisphere). After this it follows the expected curve until the next autumn minimum, but, of course, it never reaches the high values found near the North Pole in March. Measurements of the upper air temperatures show that the upper part of the stratosphere at the South Pole is very cold in winter and remains cold during the spring and then suddenly, close to the time of the ozone 'jump' in November, the temperature at the highest levels rises sharply and within a few weeks may have risen 50 °C. The change of temperature in the lower stratosphere is smaller and less sudden. Clearly, during November the whole structure of the south polar stratosphere has undergone a fundamental change. It seems as if in winter the south polar stratosphere is cut off from the general world-wide circulation of air by the very intense vortex of strong westerly winds which blow round the Antarctic continent, enclosing very cold air which is rather weak in ozone; neither the ozone nor the temperature rises much until this vortex suddenly breaks down in November. However, much further work will be necessary before these conditions are fully understood.

(2) The second anomaly is found in high latitudes in Canada. Here sudden rises both in the temperature of the stratosphere and in the total ozone are also found, but while near the South Pole the change has so far always taken place in November, in north Canada the rise may be found at any time between January and April. At Spitzbergen the seasonal variation seems to be more normal, though the rise in ozone during January and February is generally rapid. Clearly neither the sudden warming nor the increase in ozone can be due directly to solar radiation, for in Canada the rise can occur at times when the sun is still below the horizon and in no case could the solar heating produce so rapid a warming. Both the warming and the increase in ozone are almost certainly due to descending air in the upper

stratosphere which causes a warming of the air by compression and carries down ozone-rich air into the lower stratosphere. Another abnormality appears to exist in north India where the ozone values seem to be consistently lower than those at similar latitudes in America, Africa, and Japan.

E. *Fall-out from Thermonuclear Explosions*

A rather striking confirmation of the circulation of the air in the stratosphere, which was suggested by the study of atmospheric ozone and humidity, has recently come from measurements of the fall-out of radioactive materials from thermonuclear explosions. While the earlier atomic explosions projected radioactive matter into the upper troposphere, from where it fell out, or was washed out, in a matter of weeks, the larger, thermonuclear explosions projected radioactive matter right up into the upper stratosphere from where it only slowly returned to the earth. The fall-out of the long-lived radioactive elements has been measured in many different parts of the world and its variations show striking resemblances to those of atmospheric ozone. In the first place, although many of the explosions took place in low northern latitudes, most of the fall-out was found in middle latitudes and very little radio-active matter came down near the equator. It is remarkable that even the small amount of radioactive material which drifted across the equator into the southern hemisphere fell out in greater quantities in middle southern latitudes than nearer the equator and in spring rather than in autumn. The general rising current of air in the upper troposphere and lower strato-sphere, which we have suggested exists in low latitudes, well accounts for the low fall-out in this part of the world. In view of the fact that the ozone is formed continuously at high levels all over the sunlit part of the world, while radioactive material is injected in isolated places and at definite times, it is not surprising that there is a difference in the latitude of the maxi-mum ozone and the maximum fall-out, the ozone having a maximum in high latitudes and the fall-out in middle latitudes.

The second point of interest is that the rate of fall-out in temperate latitudes shows a strong maximum in the spring (possibly slightly later than the ozone maximum) and a minimum in the autumn, almost exactly in line with the seasonal variation of ozone. Unfortunately there are few measurements of the radioactive fall-out which can be used to see whether it also follows the changes in atmospheric ozone with varying meteorological conditions, which we shall discuss in the next section, but some measurements indicate that this is the case.

5. OZONE AND WEATHER—DAY-TO-DAY VARIATIONS

A. (i) *Middle Latitudes*

Up to now we have considered the ozone values averaged over a period of a month or more and we now turn to the much more rapid variations which take place within a few days. In the same way we have previously considered only average values over wide areas of the world, averaging out the variations which are found on many days between places a few hundred miles apart. Actually the rapid, and relatively local, variations of ozone are as large as the seasonal and world-wide variations, so that on a day with relatively low ozone in spring, the ozone value may be the same as on a day with relatively high ozone in the autumn. These rapid, local variations are of great interest since they are found to be closely associated with other meteorological conditions. Since most of the ozone is known to exist above the tropopause, it is only to be expected that these short-period variations would be more closely related to the meteorological conditions in the upper atmosphere than to the surface conditions and this is found to be the case. It has been shown in Chapter 2 that there are close connections between the variations of the temperature, the pressure, the height of tropopause, and other variables in the upper atmosphere, so that we naturally find that the variations in ozone are connected with all these to a greater or less extent. There is a tendency for the following associations.

High ozone	*Low ozone*
Cyclonic wind circulation at the level of the tropopause.	Anticyclonic wind circulation at the tropopause.
High temperature in the stratosphere.	Low temperature in the stratosphere.
Low temperature in the troposphere.	High temperature in the troposphere.
Low level of tropopause.	High level of tropopause.
Low absolute pressure.	High absolute pressure.

These relations are brought out in Fig. 6.5 where 3-day running means of the ozone, the height of the 200-mb surface, and the height of the tropopause are plotted one above the other. It is found that if 3-day running mean values are used, the curves show a rather closer connection than if individual daily values

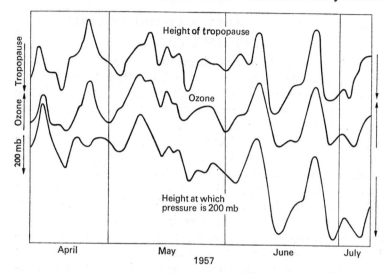

FIG. 6.5. Variations in ozone, height of the tropopause and height of the 200-mb surface.

The curves show 3-day running means of the ozone at Oxford, and also the height of the tropopause and the height of the 200-mb surface at Crawley (110 km SE. of Oxford). The top and bottom curves are plotted with heights increasing downwards to conform with the variations of ozone.

The height of the tropopause and the 200-mb surface are taken from the Aerological Record, Meteorological Office, Air Ministry, by kind permission of the Director-General.

are plotted, probably because small errors of observation are reduced but the real changes are not smoothed out too much.

While the variations in the amount of ozone are associated with changes in the height of the tropopause, etc., the closest relation of all is shown by the *type* of pressure distribution at about the height of the tropopause. On those days when the pressure maps for a height of about 9 km (300 mb) show cyclonic conditions, the amount of ozone is relatively large, while when the conditions are anticyclonic there is relatively little ozone. The 300-mb weather maps for three typical pairs of days are shown in Fig. 6.6 (*a*), (*b*), and (*c*). In each figure two contrasted days are shown, one having cyclonic and the other anticyclonic conditions. The maps give the contours of the 300-mb surface, the contours being very similar to isobars.

The absolute change in the amount of ozone between cyclonic and anticyclonic days in spring is rather greater than the corresponding change in the autumn, but since the average value of the ozone is lower in the autumn the percentage changes in spring and autumn are not very different. For those readers who are more used to seeing the weather maps for the ground level than for the upper air, it may be well to point out that systems of closed isobars showing definite areas of low pressure (cyclones) or high pressure (anticyclones) at low levels generally tend to become troughs of low pressure and ridges of high pressure in the upper atmosphere. It will be seen from these maps that the relation between the ozone and the pressure distribution is equally close at all times of the year (an important point to which we shall refer again later). It will also be seen that in the transition region between a trough and a ridge, the changes in ozone may be very rapid. On 16 March 1958, for example, the value was 0·504 cm over Denmark (cyclonic) and only 0·373 cm over England (anticyclonic). As a trough moves across the country followed by a ridge, or vice versa, one may find changes of as much as 0·100 cm between one day and the next.

(ii) *Day-to-day Changes in Tropical Regions*

It has already been pointed out that in low latitudes the total amount of ozone is everywhere small and that there is little variation from day to day. The storms that occur in low latitudes are mostly confined to the lower levels of the atmosphere and, as would be expected, do not cause any change in the total ozone. Even the change from SW. to NE. monsoon and vice versa in India is not accompanied by any appreciable change in the amount of ozone, since the monsoon does not affect the upper atmosphere. In north India during the winter months depressions may move in from middle latitudes and these give an increase in the amount of ozone just as depressions do in higher latitudes.

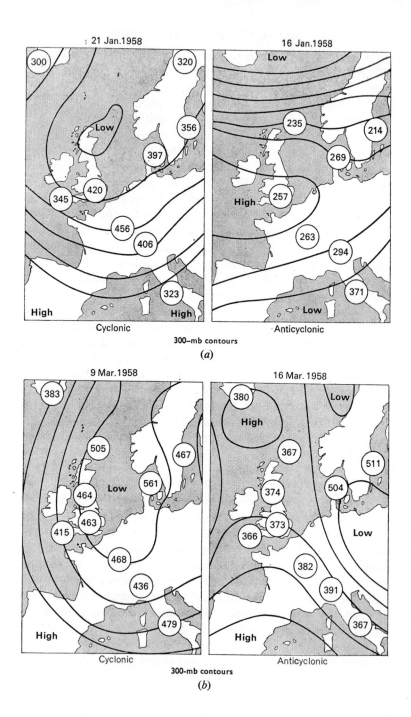

21 Jan.1958

300 320

Low

356

397

420

345

456

406

323

High   High

Cyclonic

16 Jan.1958

Low

235 214

269

High 257

263

294

371

Low

Anticyclonic

300–mb contours

(a)

9 Mar.1958

383

505

467

464 Low 561

463

415

468

436

479

High

Cyclonic

16 Mar. 1958

380 Low

High

367

511

374 504

373

366 Low

382

391

367

High

Anticyclonic

300-mb contours

(b)

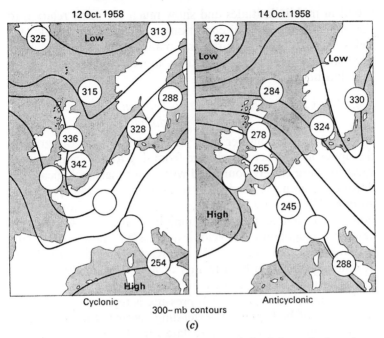

12 Oct. 1958   14 Oct. 1958

Cyclonic   Anticyclonic

300– mb contours

(c)

FIG. 6.6. Pressure distribution at the 300-mb level for cyclonic and anticyclonic days.

These three pairs of maps show the pressure distribution at a height of about 9 km by means of contours of the 300-mb surface. The figures within the circles give the values of the total ozone at each place in thousandths of a centimetre. Each pair of days contrasts cyclonic and anticyclonic conditions. The high value of the ozone in cyclonic conditions is clearly seen. The contours of the 300-mb surface are reproduced from the Aerological Record, Meteorological Office, Air Ministry, by kind permission of the Director-General, as are also the ozone values for Lerwick, Eskdalemuir, and Cambourne.

(iii) *Day-to-day Changes in Polar Regions*

Until the beginning of the International Geophysical Year (July 1957) the only measurements of the amount of ozone in very high latitudes were those at Spitzbergen (78° N.) and, owing to the very difficult conditions there, the number of observations was rather small. During the I.G.Y. measurements were made at Halley Bay (75° S.), at Alert (82·5° N.), and at Resolute (75° N.). Daily measurements at these stations can, of course, only be made during the summer half of the year but these indicate that the day-to-day changes are similar to those found in middle latitudes and show much the same relation to the other meteorological conditions as is found in middle latitudes. When all the measurements made during the I.G.Y. have been studied we may hope to know more about the changes in high latitudes.

B. *The Cause of the Connection between Ozone and other Upper Air Conditions*

We must now consider what causes the amount of ozone in the upper atmosphere to change from day to day, and why the variations are closely connected with other meteorological conditions. As with the changes in total ozone between spring and autumn, the changes between cyclonic and anticyclonic conditions are found to take place mainly in the first 5 to 10 km above the tropopause. A cyclonic depression, shown on the surface weather map as a closed low pressure area, is represented at a height of 15 km by a trough of low pressure extending to lower latitudes; on the other hand, an anticyclone, shown on the surface map as an area of high pressure is represented at 15 km by a ridge of high pressure extending towards the pole. These troughs and ridges tend to circulate round the pole from west to east, but the general westerly wind at these heights has a much greater speed, and the air actually flows *through* these troughs and ridges. As the air blows into a low pressure trough it descends, while as it approaches a ridge it ascends. These descending and ascending movements of the air will lead to increases and decreases in the amount of ozone as we have described a little earlier, and will, to some extent at least, account for the greater amount of ozone in depressions than in anticyclones. In spring—but not in autumn—the general amount of ozone is greater in high latitudes than in low latitudes, so that north polar currents will tend to carry southward air which is rich in ozone, while equatorial currents will carry polewards air which is weak in ozone. This is also a cause in producing changes in the total ozone. However, in autumn, as shown in Figs. 6.2 and 6.3, there is little change in the amount of total ozone found at any latitude north of about 45° N. so that at this season the effect will not apply. We have still much to learn about these changes in ozone.

7. The Sun, Sun-spots, and Solar Activity

I. INTRODUCTION

IN the chapters which follow we shall have to refer many times to sun-spots, to solar activity, and to solar flares. It therefore seems desirable to insert here a few notes on these solar phenomena since, though they are not part of the earth's atmosphere, yet one cannot understand the effects of the sun on the upper atmosphere without some knowledge of them. Further, the subjects of the following chapters are so much interlinked that the reader is advised to read this chapter and the following chapters straight through and then re-read them a second time since, to appreciate some of the facts given in an earlier chapter, it is necessary to know something of the subjects of the following ones.

2. THE SUN

To the astronomer the sun is just a star, one among millions of millions of stars; it is a fairly average star; there are stars that are much hotter and there are stars that are much colder; there are stars that are much bigger and there are stars that are much smaller; there are stars that are composed of matter that is very much denser and there are stars that are composed of matter that is very much rarer. Just as its properties do not make the sun stand out as in any way different from other stars, so neither does its position in our galaxy, for it is far from the centre and somewhat out of the central plane. To the meteorologist and the geophysicist, and indeed to all the inhabitants of the earth, the sun is of supreme importance as the source of all the energy required to keep the earth warm and to drive the great atmospheric 'machine', including the winds, ocean currents, thunderstorms, and all the other atmospheric activities.

The heat that is radiated away from the surface is produced deep within the sun where both the temperature and pressure are extremely high. It is generally believed that this heat is produced by the conversion of hydrogen into helium, a nuclear change releases a large amount of energy. This heat that is produced in the centre of the sun travels slowly out to the surface where it is finally radiated away. Less than one part in a thousand million of this energy falls on the earth, yet even this amounts to over a hundred thousand million MW (a large electric power station may produce about 1000 MW).

The whole sun consists of a mass of gas in which the pressure is very high at the centre and falls rapidly towards the surface. In the outermost regions, where the density is small, this gas is transparent, but as the pressure increases inwards it becomes opaque to light so that we cannot see far into the sun. While there is no definite surface above which the gas is transparent and below which it is opaque, the change takes place within a distance which is very small compared with the radius of the sun. It is for this reason that the sun appears to have a sharply defined surface. This surface which we see is known as the photosphere and is the layer from which light and by far the greater part of the solar radiation is emitted. The photosphere emits a continuous spectrum but above it is the chromosphere, which contains vapours of iron, calcium, etc., these absorb certain definite wavelengths of the light emitted by the photosphere, so that the spectrum of the sun is a continuous spectrum crossed by a large number of darker lines, known as the Fraunhofer lines.

The corona

Outside the visible surface of the sun there exists the corona, an exceedingly tenuous mass of gas. So faint is the visible light emitted by the corona that, until recently, it could only be observed during a solar eclipse when the intense light from the sun itself was cut off by the moon. Photographs taken at such times showed the corona extending out from the sun to a distance of one or two solar diameters, becoming fainter and fainter at the greater distances. Recently techniques have been developed that allow observations to be made on the corona without an eclipse, but even so it is necessary to go to a high-level observatory where the air is very clear. It is now believed that the corona extends out from the sun to very great distances, even extending as far as the earth and beyond, though as an exceedingly rare gas, mainly consisting of positively charged hydrogen atoms and electrons. Perhaps the most surprising thing about the corona is that its temperature is very high—of the order of a million degrees near the sun—far higher than that of the visible surface of the sun. Because of its very high temperature, the corona emits a considerable amount of short-wave, ultra-violet radiation, and X-rays, while, at the other end of the spectrum, the corona emits radio waves. The whole corona seems to be moving outwards from the sun.

3. SOLAR ROTATION

Another of the surprising things about the sun is that it does not rotate as a solid body would—all parts turning round in the same time—but the equatorial regions rotate faster than do the polar regions. This rotation can be measured by observing the movements of sun-spots across the visible disc of the sun, or by spectroscopic methods, and it is found that, near the solar equator, the sun rotates relative to the earth in about 25 days, while near the poles it rotates in about 35 days. This, of course, refers to the rotation of the visible surface of the sun and we know little about the rotation of the underlying layers. It is of interest to note that the planet Jupiter shows a similar change in the rate of rotation with latitude.

4. SUN-SPOTS AND THE SUN-SPOT CYCLE

If the surface of the sun is examined with a low-power telescope or a pair of binoculars (fitted with the necessary dark glass) it will be found that on some days there is nothing noteworthy to be seen, while on other days one or more small, dark markings are clearly visible. These markings are sometimes minute spots and sometimes have a clearly defined area. If a spot is followed from day to day, it may be seen to grow and then decrease again and finally disappear after a life of any-thing from a few days to a few weeks or even, occasionally, some months. The spots may be isolated but frequently they occur in pairs. Sun-spots do not appear all over the sun but are confined to two belts to the north and to the south of the equator. As has been said above, the period of rotation of the sun can be measured by watching the travel of sun-spots across the disc of the sun. If their life is long enough, they may be seen to disappear round the edge of the sun, and, after about a fortnight, to reappear round the other edge of the sun. At the average latitude of sun-spots, the sun rotates about once in 27 days relative to the earth. The temperature of the sun's surface within a sun-spot is much cooler than that around it, though still very hot by terrestrial standards. Sun-spots possess strong magnetic fields and when they occur in pairs, the leading spot has one magnetic polarity and the following one the opposite polarity.

If the number and size of the visible sun-spots are regularly recorded, it is seen that the number varies greatly. If the observations are continued for several years it is found that in some years very few spots are seen, while in other years there are nearly always some spots visible. A long series of observations shows that there is a rough periodicity of about 11 years. This is the famous 11-year sun-spot cycle. It is quite unknown to what this periodicity is due. Fig. 7.1 shows the variation in the number of sun-spots over 160 years and it will be noted that the period is not exactly constant nor do the maxima all reach the same height, though at the times of minima there are always very few spots visible. The timing of the beginning of the International Geophysical Year (July 1957) was chosen so that it would coincide with the expected time of maximum solar activity, and in fact it opened with an unusual burst of activity. The I.G.Y. proved so successful that another period of international co-operation was arranged for 1964–5—the International Quiet Sun Year (I.Q.S.Y.)—to study geophysical conditions at a time when the sun-spot cycle was at a minimum. At the beginning of a new 11-year cycle the spots tend to occur in solar latitudes of about 25° N. or 25° S. and as the cycle progresses they occur in lower and lower latitudes until near the end of the cycle most spots are seen in latitudes of about 5° N. and 5° S. At this time some spots of the next cycle can often be seen in high latitudes. The measure of the number of sun-spots visible may be given as a fraction of the sun's disc which is covered by spots, but the older 'Wolf sun-spot number' is still often used and is roughly proportional to the area of visible sun-spots. Since the sun-spot number is closely connected with other activities of the sun and, since it is easily measured, it is a very useful index of the 'activity' of the sun.

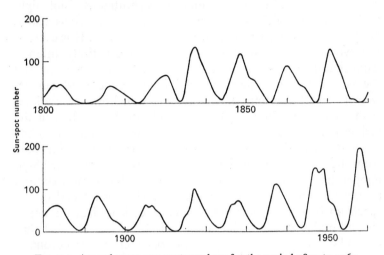

FIG. 7.1. Annual mean sun-spot numbers for the period 1800 to 1960. Note the general 11-year periodicity and also the considerable variations from one cycle to another.

5. SOLAR FLARES

Occasionally a very small and very bright patch is seen to form on the surface of the sun, often near a sun-spot, and is known as a solar flare. The increase in the radiation from a flare is very much greater in the very short, ultra-violet wavelengths than in the visible wavelengths, and small flares, which are not easily detected by the eye, may show a great increase in the far ultra-violet region. The radiation emitted by hydrogen in the sun is increased very much at the time of a flare, even those hydrogen lines which are in the visible region of the spectrum becoming brighter. Since all the ultra-violet radiation is absorbed in the upper atmosphere it cannot be observed from the ground, but a brightening of the visible hydrogen lines can give an indication of the existence of a flare. Flares are very short-lived; they may reach their full brightness in a few minutes and then die away again within an hour.

6. SOLAR RADIATION (WAVE RADIATION)

The largest part of the sun's radiation is emitted as visible light and in this part of the spectrum it radiates very much as a solid body would do at a temperature of about 6000 °C. However, at the two ends of the spectrum its radiation is entirely different from that given out by a hot solid body. In the very short and the very long wavelengths a solid body would send out extremely small amounts of energy; the sun, however, radiates strongly in both these regions—though much less than in the visible part of the spectrum. The radio waves emitted by the sun and much of the very short wave ultra-violet radiation come from the solar corona which, as we have seen, is at a very high temperature, and, though very tenuous, is able to emit enough energy to be of great importance. The short-wave end of the spectrum is of particular importance since it ionizes the upper air and makes it a good conductor of electricity. The fact that the radio waves sent out by the sun originate in the corona is seen from the fact that if the source is accurately located by a radio telescope, it is often found to be entirely outside the sun's visible disc. The radio waves are of great interest but do not have any influence on the earth's atmosphere in the same way as the short waves do.

As has already been said, the greater part of the radiation emitted by the sun is in, or near, the visible part of the spectrum, and this radiation is very constant from day to day and from year to year. If there are variations they are but little larger than the errors of measurement. On the other hand, the very short wavelengths—ultra-violet light and X-rays—may vary much from day to day. These short wavelengths cannot be studied from the ground since they are all absorbed high in the atmosphere, but even before the advent of rockets and satellites, the study of the ionosphere had shown indirectly that there were large variations in their intensity and that they followed the 11-year sun-spot cycle. The very short-wave ultra-violet radiation is mostly emitted in certain definite wavelengths or spectral lines rather than as a continuous spectrum. The radio waves emitted by the sun can, of course, be studied from the ground and even when the sky is cloudy, and they have been found to vary even more than the ultra-violet wavelengths. The variations in the intensity of these radio waves may be used as a good indication of the 'activity' of the sun in the same way as the sun-spot number is used. Since the very short, ultra-violet waves and the very much longer radio waves are both associated with the corona, while the visible radiation comes from the surface of the sun, it is not surprising that the former may be very variable while the latter are very constant, their origins being quite different.

7. SOLAR RADIATION (CORPUSCULAR RADIATION)

In the previous section we discussed the electro-magnetic, or wave radiation from the sun; there is, however, an entirely different type of radiation which is also of importance for our purpose, namely a corpuscular radiation, consisting of particles and not of waves. These particles are mostly positively charged hydrogen atoms and electrons, and they are shot out at very high speeds and, at times, in large quantities. The speed of many of the particles is such that they take about a day or two to travel from the sun to the earth (light takes about 8 min), though some are slower and, at times, some are much faster. Solar flares and areas near sun-spots are particularly active in sending out this corpuscular radiation. At the time of a very intense solar flare particles may be shot out with very high speeds, approaching that of the slower particles in cosmic radiation. It appears that there are also certain special areas on the sun that are active in this way though they cannot be identified visually; these are the so-called M regions which are described in Chapter 10. The existence of these M regions is inferred from the effects of corpuscular radiation on the earth's magnetic field which show a 27-day period, even at times when there are no sun-spots visible. Clearly the 27-day period can be identified with the period of solar rotation, and the increased radiation received by the earth would seem to be due to certain active areas coming opposite to the earth at each solar rotation. This corpuscular radiation is the cause of magnetic disturbance, the aurora, and disturbances in the ionosphere.

It was mentioned earlier that the number of sun-spots that are visible at any time is a useful measure of the 'activity' of the sun. This is shown in Fig. 7.2 where the quarterly mean sun-spot number for the years 1922–40 is plotted above the quarterly

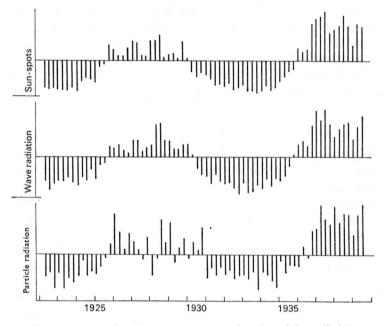

FIG. 7.2. Connection between sun-spots, solar ultra-violet radiation, and solar corpuscular radiation.

In each case the difference of the mean value for each quarter of the year from the mean for the whole period is plotted as the length of the vertical lines, upwards for values above the mean and downwards for values below the mean.

means of the solar activity as measured by (1) the intensity of the short-wave radiation and (2) by the intensity of the sun's corpuscular radiation reaching the earth. (The way in which these are estimated will be described in Chapter 10.) In this figure the differences of the quarterly mean values from the general mean value are plotted as the lengths of the lines upwards or downwards. The agreement between the sun-spots and the wave-radiation is particularly close. If monthly mean values had been used instead of quarterly means the agreement would have been less close, while if daily values had been used little connection would have been shown in the individual values.

8. THE SOLAR WIND

As mentioned in the section on the corona, there is always a stream of hydrogen atoms and electrons moving outwards from the sun at a speed of a few hundred kilometres per second. This is often known as the solar wind. The streams of particles sent out at the times of solar flares and other solar disturbances, which cause the aurora and magnetic storms, are much more intense and have much greater speeds.

It is well known that the tails of comets point more or less away from the sun, both when the comets are approaching the sun and also when they are moving away from it. At one time it was thought that this was due to the pressure of sunlight on the small particles and gases which form the tails of comets, but it now seems more likely that the tail is blown away from the head of the comet by the solar wind.

It will be seen in later chapters that there is reason for dividing the emission of charged particles from the sun into three classes:

(1) The continuous solar wind, which consists of relatively few slow-moving particles and is fairly uniform in time and direction, but probably varies with the 11-year sun-spot period.

(2) The sudden emission of large numbers of particles at high speeds from solar flares. These appear to be emitted over a wide angle but last for only a relatively short time.

(3) The emission of charged particles in a narrower beam from certain 'active' regions, but these show no visible markings on the sun's disc. They are usually known as M regions and last for a long time—two or more 27-day solar rotation periods.

8. The Ionosphere

As we shall describe more fully in Chapter 10, as early as 1882 it had been suggested that somewhere in the upper atmosphere the air was a good conductor of electricity. This suggestion was put forward to explain the small regular, diurnal variations that were observed in the earth's magnetic field. At that time, of course, nothing was known about the ionosphere and little further was discovered until the advent of radio. In the very early days of radio it was a great surprise when it was discovered that radio signals could be transmitted round the curved surface of the earth. Radio waves, like light waves, normally travel in straight lines, and there must be some special cause to make them bend round the earth. The suggestion of an electrically conducting region, high in the atmosphere, now received strong support, for such a conducting region would act rather like a mirror and would reflect back to the ground radio waves that had travelled into the upper atmosphere. The position is, indeed, rather analogous to the reflection of sound waves by the warm region at a height of 50 km which we described in Chapter 3, but in this case the radio waves are bent because of the presence of electrons in the upper air, while the sound waves were bent because of the increasing temperature of the air. Just as it is possible to explore the temperature of the upper atmosphere by measuring the return of sound waves which have been reflected by the upper warm region, so it is possible to measure the electron content of the ionosphere by measuring the return of radio waves that have been reflected back to earth. However, there is one very important difference, namely that since radio waves travel so much faster than sound, the time intervals to be measured are very short. By far the most convenient instrument for measuring these short intervals of time is the cathode-ray oscillograph, and we shall briefly describe how this instrument works.

2. METHODS OF EXPLORING THE IONOSPHERE

A. *The Cathode-ray Oscillograph*

A narrow beam of fast-moving electrons (cathode rays) is emitted by an 'electron gun', E (see Fig. 8.1), at one end of an evacuated tube and, after travelling along the axis of the tube,

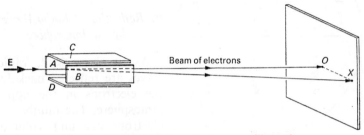

FIG. 8.1. Principle of the cathode-ray oscillograph.

A narrow beam of electrons, shot out from E, passes between the deflecting plates A, B, and C, D. When an electric potential is applied between A and B the beam of electrons is deflected so that it falls on the fluorescent screen at X instead of at O.

falls on a fluorescent screen at the opposite end of the tube. A small bright spot of light is produced where the electrons strike the fluorescent material at O. Soon after leaving the 'gun', the electron beam passes between two pairs of insulated metal plates arranged like the sides of an open-ended box. A, B and C, D. If an electric field is set up between the plates A and B, the electrons in the beam will be deflected sideways, so that instead of falling on the screen at O, they fall at the point X.

The instrument is arranged so that the spot of light normally rests at a point near one side of the screen, and then at a given signal, it is made to start moving sideways at a uniform speed across the screen, by applying a constantly increasing voltage between the plates A and B. The spot of light may be made to traverse the screen at any required speed, e.g. in 1 s or 1/10 000 s, or any other short time. On reaching the far side of the screen, the spot is made to jump back to its starting place. Since the screen remains luminous for a short time, the spot appears to draw a bright line across the screen. If, while the spot is travelling across the screen, an electric voltage is applied momentarily between the plates C and D, the spot will be deflected up or down and a 'pip' will be produced on the line (see Fig. 8.2). The distance of the 'pip' from the starting point will be a measure of the time between the signal which started the beam moving and that which produced the 'pip'.

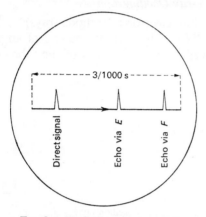

FIG. 8.2. Typical appearance of the screen of a cathode-ray oscillograph.

B. *Reflection of Radio Waves by the Ionosphere*

As we have said, radio waves are reflected back by the electrons in the upper atmosphere. The number of electrons per unit volume, which is necessary to reflect radio waves in this way, depends both on the angle at which the radio waves strike the ionosphere and the frequency of the waves. In most of the work we shall describe the radio waves travel vertically upwards and are returned directly downwards, thus striking the ionosphere normally. Since in the lower part of the ionosphere the density of electrons is increasing with height, the radio waves will travel upwards until they reach a place where there are just enough electrons to reflect them back again.

C. *An Imaginary Experiment*

The way in which the ionosphere is explored may be most easily understood if we describe an imaginary experiment. Fig. 8.3. shows a transmitter T which sends very short pulses of radio waves up into the upper atmosphere. These are reflected by the ionosphere—whose electron density is indicated by shading—and are detected by the receiver R on the ground. We set the cathode-ray oscillograph so that the spot of light travels the full course from left to right in about 3/1000 s. We now start the experiment by setting the frequency of the transmitter and receiver to rather more than 1 Mc/s (300-m wavelength) and send out one pulse of radio waves. The pulse, which is immediately picked up by the adjacent receiver, starts the electron beam of the oscillograph moving and also produces a 'pip' (Fig. 8.2). The spot of light is now travelling rapidly across the

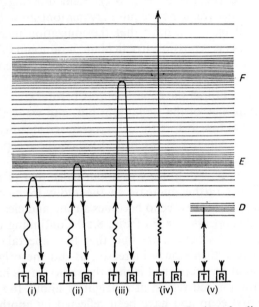

FIG. 8.3. Diagrammatic representation of the reflection of radio waves
from the ionosphere.

T is a radio transmitter, R is a radio receiver. The intensity of ionization in
the ionosphere is indicated by shading.

screen from left to right, and after rather less than a thousandth of a second an echo will be received from the ionosphere which will produce a second 'pip', *E*, about a quarter of the way across the screen. Careful timing will show that the echo has travelled about 200 km so that it was reflected back at a height of about 100 km (see ray (i) of Fig. 8.3). Next we adjust the frequency of the radio transmitter to a slightly higher value and send out another pulse. Again the cathode ray oscillograph will show both the initial pulse and its echo, but in this case the mark of the echo will be slightly farther away from that of the initial pulse. This shows that the time taken has been rather longer, so that the radio pulse must have gone to a rather greater height before being reflected back again. We now continue the experiment, always increasing the frequency of the transmitter a little before sending out the next pulse, and we shall find that the interval of time before the echo is received continues to increase (see ray (ii) of Fig. 8.3). Remembering that radio waves of higher frequency require greater ionization before they are reflected back, we infer that the ionization increases with height and, as it is possible to calculate the amount of ionization that will just reflect a radio wave of any given frequency, we can plot a curve showing the ionization at each height.

We now continue the experiment as before, steadily increasing the frequency of the signal sent out, and we shall find that the interval of time before the echo is received steadily increases. But soon a frequency is reached at which the reception of the echo becomes doubtful and erratic, and signs of another echo begin to appear with a delay of about twice that of the former echo. With a further increase in the radio frequency of the emitted pulse, this new echo becomes strong and clear while the old echo disappears (see F of Fig. 8.2). Continuing to increase the frequency as before, we find that the time taken for this new echo to return slowly increases, as did the original echo. Clearly, what has happened is that the radio waves have passed through the ionized region at a height of about 100 km which gave the first echo and have been reflected by another ionized region at a greater height (see ray (iii) of Fig. 8.3). The lower of these ionized regions is known as the E region, while the higher is known as the F region. If we still continue to increase the frequency of the radio pulses, the echoes take longer and longer to come back and finally, after a rapid increase of the time interval, no echoes are received at all. At this point we have reached a frequency such that there is no region in the atmosphere with sufficient ionization to reflect these radio waves and they pass right out through the atmosphere into space (see ray (iv) of Fig. 8.3).

In order to get a continuous picture of the electrical state of the ionosphere, it is usual to devise an apparatus which automatically sends out a stream of pulses whose radio frequency gradually increases from about 1 to 20 Mc/s, and then starts again at the lower frequency, repeating the process indefinitely.

The position of the pips on the oscillograph is recorded photographically. As has been stated above, the height at which the radio pulse is reflected is deduced from the time it takes to travel up and back again. Although in free space radio waves travel with the same velocity as light, when they pass through an ionized region they travel slower, and this must be kept in mind when deducing the actual height of reflection. The decrease in velocity is particularly marked when the number of electrons present is only just a little more or less than the number required to reflect the radio waves. This produces an anomalous increase in the delay of the echo at frequencies near those which just penetrate the E and F layers.

Another method which has been used is to employ high-power vertical radar and to measure the intensity of the radio waves *scattered* back from different levels in the ionosphere, when the intensity of the scattered waves is a measure of the electron density at the height of scattering. The height of scattering is obtained from the delay of the echo as usual.

Long-distance radio transmission is possible by using the forward (and downward) scattering of short wavelengths by the ionosphere. Since such waves have usually passed through the D region the intensity of the received signal may be used to estimate the absorption—and therefore the ionization—of the D region.

An entirely different method which is now being much used is to measure the intensity of cosmic radio waves which are constantly reaching the earth from the galaxy. These radio waves will be absorbed as they come down through the D region, so that low intensity of cosmic radio waves received at the ground means strong absorption by the D region. These instruments are generally known as riometers (relative ionospheric opacity meters). The wavelength used must, of course, be short enough always to penetrate the densest part of the ionosphere. The results are very useful and will be discussed in the last part of this chapter when we describe the ionosphere in disturbed conditions.

D. *Measurement of the Ionization in the Upper part of the Ionosphere*

The methods described above, except for that using the back-scatter of radio-waves, cannot be used to measure the ionozation at heights above the level of the F_2 maximum, since no radio signals are reflected back from a region where the intensity of ionization is decreasing upwards. It is possible to get some information from observations of radio waves coming into the atmosphere from outside, e.g. from 'radio stars'. It is also possible to get some information about the ionization at very great heights above the earth from the curious phenomenon of 'whistlers' or 'whistling atmospherics'. When using suitable low-frequency receivers, radio atmospherics may sometimes be heard which have a note that rapidly decreases in pitch—hence the term 'whistler'. These come from lightning flashes in distant parts of the earth. Lightning flashes send out radio waves of such very low frequence as to be within the audible range and such exceptionally long waves are guided through the upper ionosphere along the lines of the earth's magnetic force. The resulting atmospheric is thus heard at a place in the opposite hemisphere where the line of force returns to earth again. The speed of travel of these exceptional waves through the ionized region depends on their wavelength, the longer waves travelling more slowly, so that the higher frquencies are heard first and the lower frequencies later.

Instruments, which are similar in principle to those described at the beginning of this chapter for measuring the ionization at different levels in the ionosphere by signals of varying wavelength, transmitted from the ground, are now being flown on satellites. These instruments explore the ionosphere below them from some height well above the main ionosphere, and can therefore measure the ionization in the upper part that is inaccessible from ground-level stations. They have the advantage that they can cover the whole world twice a day instead of giving measurements for one place only. Against this they cannot study continuously the changes taking place in the ionosphere at a given place but only at intervals of about 12 hours. Rockets have also been used to measure the ionization of the atmosphere through which they pass, but since they can obtain measurements at one time only, they are much less useful than satellites.

3. A GENERAL PICTURE OF THE IONOSPHERE IN 'QUIET' CONDITIONS

A. *The E and F Regions*

The distribution of ionization in the ionosphere is very complex; it varies with the time of day, with the time of the year, with the 11-year sun-spot cycle, and with the state of 'activity' of the sun. Fig. 8.4 has been drawn to give the reader a picture of typical conditions in the ionosphere. On the left of this diagram the ionization, or the number of electrons per cubic centimetre, at different heights is shown by the curves for day-time and night-time conditions. On the right of the diagram, the intensity of ionization at any height is shown more pictorially by means of shading—the heavier the shading, the greater the ionization. In studying this diagram it must be remembered that it represents average conditions only, and at any time the ionization may be greater or less than that indicated, though the heights of the different regions do not change much, except for that of the F_2 region which, at times, may be higher than shown here. The most significant features which stand out in the diagram are the four bulges (D, E, F_1, and F_2), or regions of high ionization, in the day-time curve and the two bulges (E and F) at night. These different ionized regions are usually known by the letters which have been placed alongside them in the diagram, but the E region is also known as the Kennelly-Heaviside region, and the F region as the Appleton region, after their discoverers. It will be seen that the F_1 region is not separated from the F_2 region by a definite minimum, but its properties are so very different from those of the F_2 region (as we shall describe shortly) that it must be regarded as a truly separate region. During the night the D region disappears, the ionization of the E region is much reduced, and that of the F_1 region is reduced enough to make it indistinguishable from the F_2 region and the two become a single F region.

The number of electrons and ions in the ionosphere is always much smaller than the number of neutral atoms and molecules at the same level, even up to 1000 km or more. Further, although in the exosphere, collisions between neutral atoms or molecules are rare, and the mean free path is very long, so that neutral particles generally follow ballistic paths, travelling up and down

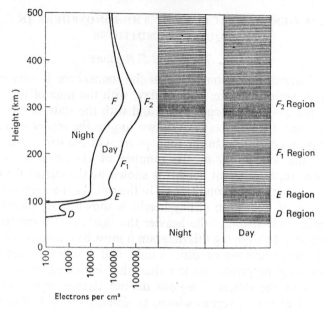

FIG. 8.4. Intensity of ionization at different levels in the iosonphere.

The curves show the general way in which the number of electrons varies with height both at night and during the day. The ionization is also shown by shading. The conditions vary greatly with the sun-spot number, with the season of the year, and with the solar activity so that only a general indication can be given.

again without a collision; this is not the case with electrons and ions. Owing to the electric forces between these charged particles, they affect each other at much greater distances than neutral particles and their mean free path is relatively small.

B. *The D Region*

Up to now we have made little mention of the *D* region of the ionosphere, and before we can discuss it properly it is necessary to make a slight digression. When radio waves pass up into the ionosphere they cause the electrons which are there to oscillate (it is really this oscillation which causes the reflection of the radio waves). In these higher regions of the ionosphere the mean free path of the electrons is very long and they can oscillate relatively freely, without too many collisions with air molecules. Lower down, in the *D* region, where there are many more air molecules, the mean free path of the electrons is much shorter and here, when they begin to oscillate, they collide frequently with air molecules. The result is that the energy that an electron picked up from a radio wave and that made it oscillate is quickly handed over to the air molecules and this causes a very slight warming of the air and an absorption of the radio waves. Radio waves passing through the D region therefore tend to be absorbed and not reflected, as they are in the higher regions of the ionosphere. While it is possible, by using radio transmitters of very high power and other techniques, to get some reflection from the D region, it is naturally much more difficult to investigate than the higher regions and much less is known about it (see Fig. 8.3 ray (v). Many people will be familiar with the fact that by day a medium-wave, local broadcasting station can be heard without interference, but after sunset some distant foreign station working on a similar wavelength often begins to come in also and may be very difficult to eliminate. This is due to the fact that distant stations are generally heard by means of radio waves which have gone up into the ionosphere and have there been reflected down again. During the day-time, such radio waves are absorbed by the D region and so give no trouble, but after dark, the D region disappears and the distant station is heard strongly.

c. *Regular Annual and Diurnal Variations of the Ionosphere in 'Quiet' Conditions*

The intensity of ionization in the ionosphere shows well-marked annual and diurnal variations, those of the D, E, and F_1 regions following closely the height of the sun. On the other hand, the F_2 region shows no such simple regularities, indeed at times the changes are in the opposite direction to those expected. There is evidence that if the total number of electrons within the F_2 region is considered, rather than the concentration of electrons at a given height, then greater regularity is found. As an example of the curious behaviour of the F_2 region we may cite the variation of the electron density with latitude. The maximum density of the electrons in the F_2 region is found to increase from high latitudes towards the magnetic equator, but within $10°$ of the magnetic equator there is a marked minimum in the midday values. (For definition of the magnetic equator see Chapter 10.) It should be noted that this peculiarity follows the magnetic equator and not the geographical equator. In South America the magnetic equator is as much as $15°$ south of the geographical equator. It thus appears that the magnetic field of the earth in some way affects the ionization of the F_2 region as well as short-wave radiation from the sun. It is shown in Chapter 3 that at the height of the F_2 region there is a very large diurnal variation of temperature with a maximum soon after noon and a minimum around sunrise. The very high day-time temperature will cause the air to expand and also reduce the density of electrons in the F_2 region.

D. *The 11-year Sun-spot Period*

The intensity of ionization of the ionosphere follows the 11-year sun-spot period closely. Even the F_2 region—otherwise often so irregular—shows this connection so that there is little doubt about the solar control of this region also; other factors seem to be responsible for producing the irregularities in its ionization.

4. THE CAUSE OF THE IONIZATION IN THE IONOSPHERE

In Chapter 5 it was shown that the ionization in the lower layers of the atmosphere is largely produced by cosmic radiation and that the ionization so produced increases with increasing height, since this radiation comes in from outside the atmosphere. The intensity of the ionization in the ionosphere is far greater than that in the troposphere and lower stratosphere and has a totally different origin. The close relation which has been shown to hold between the intensity of ionization and the height of the sun, leaves little room for doubt that the ionization of the lower part of the ionosphere is caused by wave-radiation from the sun (which travels with the speed of light). The decrease in the ionization of these regions at the time of a solar eclipse (see Fig. 8.5) makes this almost certain. As in other cases, the effect of an eclipse on the F_2 region is anomalous for reasons which are not yet fully understood, though changes in temperature of the air resulting from the eclipse may have an effect.

When the short-wave solar radiation passes through the highest layers of the atmosphere, it will be but little absorbed because there is little air there to absorb it, so the amount of ionization produced will be small. When the radiation reaches lower levels, where there is much more air, it will be more strongly absorbed, producing much more ionization. After

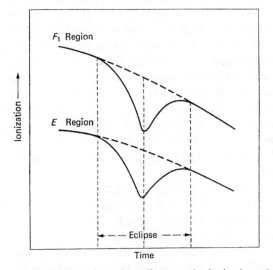

FIG. 8.5. Typical effect of a solar eclipse on the ionization of the E and F_1 regions of the ionosphere.

passing through these layers the intensity of the solar radiation will be greatly reduced so that, although there is much more air at the lower levels, little ionization will be produced. There will thus be some level where the rate of ionization is a maximum. The height of this level will depend on how strongly the ionizing radiation is absorbed, which again depends on the wavelength of the radiation. In practice many wavelengths will contribute to the ionization, so that the actual vertical distribution of ionization will be the result of all these different wavelengths. Further the rate of destruction of ionization will be greater where the density of the air is high, i.e. at the lower levels.

We must now consider which wavelengths in the solar radiation are likely to be responsible for the ionization and which gases in the atmosphere absorb this radiation and in consequence become ionized. In order that radiation may produce ionization, two things are necessary. (1) The incoming radiation must clearly be able to penetrate the upper layers of the atmosphere down to the ionized region in question and be absorbed there. (2) The wavelength of the radiation must be shorter than some particular value, which varies from one gas to another since, for any given gas, only radiation whose wavelength is shorter than a certain critical value is able to eject electrons from the atoms. It is now thought that the E and F_1 regions are produced by solar radiation in the X-ray region having wavelengths of the order of 100 Ångstrom units. If the sun radiated as an ordinary solid body at its temperature of some 6000 °C, the amount of such radiation from it would be negligible but, as mentioned in Chapter 7, it is known that the energy actually emitted in these wavelengths is far greater than would be expected. These wavelengths would penetrate to the required depth into the atmosphere and they would ionize the oxygen there.

There is more uncertainty about the wavelengths which produce the D region. The shortest radiation from the sun, of the order of 10 Ångstrom units, could penetrate down to this level and would produce the ionization of the D region if it had enough energy, but this seems doubtful except at times of solar flares. Another possibility is that the very strong radiation which is given out by hydrogen in the sun, at a wavelength of 1216 Ångstrom units (known as the Lyman alpha line), produces the D region. For most wavelengths in this region of the spectrum, the air is not transparent enough to allow them to reach such a low level, but by a coincidence, the air is more transparent just at this wavelength, so that this wavelength could penetrate to the D region. However, radiation of a wavelength of 1216 Ångstrom units is too long to ionize the more common constituents of the atmosphere. This radiation would, however, ionize nitric oxide, and it is known that there is a small amount of nitric oxide in the upper air. It may be, therefore, that the strong solar radiation in the Lyman alpha line, which is known from rocket observations to exist in solar radiation entering the outer atmosphere, may ionize the nitric oxide and so produce the D region. The general view at present is that cosmic rays may produce most of the ionization in the lowest part of the D region, while Lyman alpha radiation is important in the middle part and X-rays in the upper part. There is, however, still some uncertainty about this. The ionization of the D region is known to vary much with the sun-spot cycle but, on the other hand, the Lyman alpha radiation, as measured by satellites outside the atmosphere, varies only a little.

Little is known about the cause of the F_2 region and several different suggestions have been put forward. At present the most probable suggestion seems to be that the F_2 ionization is produced by the same type of solar radiation as that which produces the E and F_1 regions, and that it is the nature of the atmosphere at these great heights (probably the slower recombination of ions and electrons, or attachment of electrons to atoms) and not a difference in the ionizing agency which results in a separate F_2 region in the day-time.

There is another important difference between the ionization of the air in the ionosphere and that in the troposphere and lower stratosphere which must be mentioned. It will have been noticed that when speaking of the ionization of the lower regions we always referred to *ions* (i.e. molecules which had lost or gained one electron) while when speaking of the ionosphere we always referred to *electrons*. In the lower atmosphere, an electron that has been removed from a molecule rapidly becomes attached to another molecule, so that only a very small number of electrons are free at any one time. In the ionosphere, where the molecules are much further apart, free electrons can exist for a much longer time without becoming attached to molecules or atoms, so that at these greater heights free electrons and ions exist together. However, the small, fast-moving electrons are so much more effective than the heavier, slow-moving ions, that the characteristics of the ionosphere are mainly due to the electrons.

5. DISTURBED CONDITIONS IN THE IONOSPHERE

Up to now we have described the ionosphere and its regular diurnal and annual changes when the sun is 'quiet', i.e. when there are no major sun-spots or solar flares. When the sun is 'disturbed' or 'active', i.e. when there are sun-spots and solar flares, the ionosphere is also disturbed. The most important effect on the ionosphere is the complete 'blackout' of long distance, short-wave, radio communication that may occur in extreme cases. When the sun is quiet, the ionization of the upper atmosphere is caused by short-wave solar radiation, but when the sun is disturbed, additional ionization is produced both by increased short-wave radiation and also by radiation of charged particles. Both these types of radiation are often associated with a solar flare. The bursts of very short-wave radiation travel with the velocity of light so that the disturbance that is caused in the ionosphere occurs at the same time as the flare is seen. The particle radiation travels more slowly and does not usually reach the earth until a day or two after the flare, though very occasionally charged particles are sent out with speeds not much less than that of light. One of the most notable cases was on 23 February 1956 when the ionosphere on the *dark* side of the earth was disturbed only a very short time after the flare which caused it. Since the wave radiation travels in straight lines it can fall only on the daylight side of the earth, but the charged particles will be deflected by the earth's magnetic field so that they may enter the atmosphere on either the light or dark side of the earth. They will also tend to be deflected towards the earth's magnetic poles.

Although all the regions of the ionosphere are affected by disturbances, the most important effects are produced in the *D* region. When the sun is quiet the ionization in the *D* region is produced by short-wave radiation that penetrates the atmosphere down to a level of about 70 km and, because of the relatively short mean free path of electrons at this level, the radio waves passing through it tend to be absorbed, and long distance communication by short wavelengths is more difficult during the day-time than during the night, since after dark the positive ions and the electrons quickly recombine and the ionization disappears. At the time of a solar flare the ultra-violet radiation of a wavelength about 1215 Å is not much changed but radiation of shorter wavelength—possibly about 10 Å—is greatly increased, and these very short wavelengths penetrate down to about 60 km where they produce intense ionization. This region will then very strongly absorb radio waves passing through it and hence cause a 'radio black-out'. Since this short-wave radiation travels with the velocity of light, the radio black-out occurs at the same time as the flare.

While the D region tends to absorb radio waves of medium length, it reflects very long waves very well, specially if these strike it at a small angle. Lightning flashes send out very long radio waves which produce the well-known 'atmospherics', and if the D region is unusually well developed, atmospherics are heard from greater distances than usual. A sudden increase in the number of atmospherics as recorded on a suitable radio receiver, can be used to give astronomers, who are studying solar flares and their effects, a warning that a flare is starting.

Some very intense solars flares emit very high-speed protons—hydrogen nuclei—which are often known as solar cosmic rays since they have speeds only a little less than the normal cosmic rays. Although these protons have very high speeds, they are relatively few in number and, owing to their electric charge, they are deflected by the earth's magnetic field so that they fall on the atmosphere in an area around the magnetic poles. Here they penetrate the atmosphere down to about the level of the D region where they produce a general faint glow—the 'polar glow'. They also ionize the air and, as in the case of the normal D region, they cause absorption of radio waves and produce the 'polar cap absorption' which may interrupt radio communication in cases where the radio waves pass near the poles.

In addition to the effect described above, large solar flares may emit great clouds of ionized gas—protons and electrons—and while their speed is much less than that of the solar cosmic rays, their numbers are far greater. Such clouds of ionized gas take 1 to 2 days to reach the earth, but when they strike the atmosphere they cause a disturbance in all the regions of the ionosphere. In the E and F_1 regions the ionization is increased, but in the F_2 region—as so often happens—the effects are different and the ionization may be decreased. Since the intense ionization of the D region at times of a solar flare often makes it impossible to get echoes back from the F_2 region, not very much is known about these disturbances on the F_2 region, but at times the ionization is certainly much reduced. Measurements using satellites should prove very useful for this study since, of course, they are not troubled by the absorption in the D region.

It is known from measurements of the air drag on earth satellites that the temperature of the higher atmosphere is much increased at the time of solar flares and it may be that the

M

decreased ionization of the F_2 region is caused by the consequent general expansion of the air, which will reduce the density of the electrons just as it reduces the density of the neutral air molecules. However, the effects of solar disturbance on the F_2 region are very complex and depend on latitude, season, and time of day, and much still remains to be found out about them. It will be seen in the Chapter on geomagnetism that the cloud of ionized gas from a solar flare also produces magnetic storms so that disturbances in the ionosphere and the earth's magnetic field are closely connected.

9. The Aurora and the Airglow

THE AURORA

I. HEIGHT AND GEOGRAPHICAL POSITION OF THE AURORA

A. *World-wide Distribution of Visible Auroras*

The auroral belts

IN Chapter 10, on the Earth's Magnetism, it will be shown that the general magnetic field of the earth (i.e. the field that exists at such a distance from the earth that it is not affected by local irregularities) is approximately that which would be found if the earth contained a large bar magnet whose axis cut the earth's surface in the northern hemisphere at about 78·5° N. and 69° W., and at a corresponding place in the southern hemisphere.† These points are known as the geomagnetic poles. Now if we plot on a map the percentage number of nights on which the aurora is seen at different places compared with the number of nights on which it could have been seen, allowing for cloudiness and the length of daylight, we find that there are two belts, one round each pole, where the aurora is most frequently seen. Each belt is centred, not on the geographical pole, but on the geo-magnetic pole. These belts have a radius of between 20 and 25°, and at places situated on the belts, the aurora is seen on most clear nights. Because of the paucity of observations, the position of the belt of maximum frequency is less well known in the southern hemisphere than in the northern hemisphere. At places both inside and outside the belts, the aurora is seen less frequently; in Europe, for example, the belt of maximum frequency passes through south Iceland where the frequency is

---

† A still closer representation of the actual magnetic field of the earth is obtained if the axis of the assumed internal bar magnet does not pass quite through the centre of the earth, but is displaced some 300 km to one side.

almost 100 per cent; in central Scotland the frequency has fallen to about 10 per cent, while in central France it is about 1 per cent. Inside the auroral belt the frequency falls as one approaches the geomagnetic pole, and at the pole the aurora is only seen on about 20 per cent of clear nights. Since the northern geomagnetic pole is situated on 69° W. longitude, the lines of equal auroral frequency come to lower geographical latitudes over Canada than over Siberia. Outside the northern auroral belt the aurora is generallly seen in the northern sky, while at places inside the belt it is more often seen in the southern sky. At places on the auroral belt it is frequently seen overhead. The smaller auroral displays are mostly confined to places near the auroral belts, but great auroras come to much lower latitudes.

B. *The Height of the Aurora*

The height of the aurora can be measured by taking simultaneous photographs from two or more places separated by a distance of a few dozen miles. The photographic stations are linked by telephone so that the different stations take photographs of the same part of the aurora at the same time. The stars also appear on the photographs and serve as useful points of reference for the measurements. In this way the positions of many thousands of auroras have been fixed. Most measurements have been made in Scandinavia, Canada, or Alaska because of their advantageous position in relation to the auroral belts, and the name of the late Professor Störmer of Oslo will always be linked with such measurements in view of his pioneering work and the many thousands of measurements which he made over a long period of years. The heights of the base of the auroras show a very strong maximum at just over 100 km, the number of auroras extending below this height falling off very fast and few coming below 85 km. On the other hand, the upper parts of the auroral rays may reach very great heights, as much as 1000 km having been measured occasionally, though most auroras do not reach much more than about 500 km; only those auroras that occur in the part of the atmosphere that is lit by sunlight go to the great heights. Those auroras that are in sunlight have an average height of about 300 km and do not show so sharp a lower boundary as those in the lower, dark part of the atmosphere. Occasionally auroral rays are seen extending down through the sunlit atmosphere into the dark region, but these often have a break at about the height of the shadow level.

c. *Geographical Position of Individual Auroras*

The simultaneous photographs of auroras taken from two or more places give not only the height but also the geographical location of the auroras relative to the surface of the earth. It is found that the long horizontal arcs lie approximately on segments of circles whose centre is the geomagnetic pole, so that they lie at right angles to the direction of the horizontal magnetic force. These long arcs may be 1000 km or more in length and stretch from horizon to horizon. When these same arcs are viewed from directly underneath, they are seen to be quite narrow bands, of the order of a kilometre wide, and at times there may be two or more individual bands running parallel to each other a short distance apart. In high magnetic latitudes of North America there is evidence that the position of the auroras, when projected on to the earth's surface, may lie in loops that curve back over the magnetic pole, and that the auroras remain roughly stationary with respect to the sun, as the earth rotates daily beneath them. When photographs can be taken from satellites showing the distribution of the aurora over the whole of the polar region, this question should become much clearer. There is no doubt that the long vertical auroral rays follow the lines of the earth's magnetic field and curve southwards as they rise upwards in the northern hemisphere.

2. THE CAUSE OF THE AURORA

A. *Corpuscular Streams from the Sun*

In the next chapter it will be shown that the major disturbances of the earth's magnetic field are caused by streams of charged particles shot out from the sun, which fall on the outside of the atmosphere. It is thought that the aurora is caused by these same charged particles, which excite the molecules or atoms of the air. If the particles were not electrically charged they would travel in straight lines and would fall on the sunlit side of the earth only, but if they are electrically charged they will be deflected by the earth's magnetic field while still at a distance equal to several times the radius of the earth, and will tend to reach the earth on a band round each magnetic pole. It is believed that the particles are chiefly hydrogen ions (hydrogen atoms which have lost an electron) and free electrons, so that the stream as a whole is electrically neutral. Instruments carried on rockets have recently detected both hydrogen ions and electrons in the lower parts of auroras, but the emission of light seems to be caused primarily by the electrons.

It will be shown in Chapter 10 that disturbances of the earth's magnetic field are caused by particles that are ejected from two types of active areas on the sun: (a) solar flares, which are often associated with sun-spots and which cause the larger magnetic disturbances; and (b) the so-called M regions which, though they cannot be identified visually on the sun, yet seem to exist for a considerable time and cause a small magnetic disturbance when they come opposite to the earth at each solar rotation. Particles originating from both types of events on the sun produce auroras on the earth. Small auroras seem to be produced by the M regions; they show the same 27-day recurrence tendency as do small magnetic disturbances, and they do not show much effect of the 11-year cycle, or of the seasonal variation with maxima in spring and autumn, that are associated with large auroral displays.

The light from the aurora is mainly produced by the bombardment of the air by electrons, but the streams of electrons are accompanied by protons—hydrogen nuclei. In some cases very fast protons are emitted by solar flares that have such high speeds that they resemble cosmic rays and are often known as solar cosmic rays. When these protons come into the neighbourhood of the earth they are, of course, deflected by the earth's magnetic field, but they do not fall in the auroral band as the electrons do; they enter the atmosphere more or less uniformly in a small area round the magnetic poles (within, say, 10 to 20°). Here they produce a very faint uniform glow, so faint that it is difficult to detect. They also produce ionization fairly low in the ionosphere, which causes the intense absorption of radio waves —the polar cap absorption that was discussed in Chapter 8.

B. *The Spectrum of the Aurora*

We will now discuss what can be discovered about the aurora from a spectroscopic study of its light, but before starting this discussion we will make a short digression for the benefit of those readers who may not be familiar with the way in which light is emitted by gases.

(i) *Emission of light by gases*

In Chapter 3, section 3 we discussed the spectral distribution of radiation given out by hot solid bodies; the spectrum of the light given out by a gas is of an entirely different character since, while a hot solid emits light of all wavelengths and, when viewed in a spectroscope, shows a continuous spectrum from the red to the violet, the light from a gas is generally confined to certain isolated wavelengths only, so that in a spectroscope a number of bright lines or bands are seen. A gas need not be hot before it can emit light, but some of its atoms must have had one of their electrons displaced from the normal position in the atom, and when these electrons *go back* towards their normal places the energy so released is radiated away as light of a wavelength that is peculiar to the particular kind of atom. Thus a gas in which all the atoms have their electrons in their normal positions cannot emit light until something happens to displace some of the electrons, and it only emits light when these electrons return towards their normal positions in the atoms. The displacement of the electrons from their normal positions in the atoms may be caused by the absorption of light of very short wavelength, or by collisions with other fast-moving atoms or electrons. Such an action may result in the electrons being knocked right out of the atoms (when the atom becomes ionized); or the electron may be displaced to another position, but still within the atom (when the atom is said to be 'excited'). It will be seen that a hydrogen atom (which contains only one electron) cannot radiate light if it has lost this one electron (and become a hydrogen ion) until it is able to pick up another electron. We shall see shortly that this point is of some importance in the study of the auroral spectrum. Since the spectrum of the light emitted by any gas consists of certain wavelengths that are characteristic of that gas, a spectroscopic examination of the light given out by gases enables one to determine their composition.

(ii) *The auroral spectrum*

The spectrum of the aurora consists of bright lines and bands, and most of these can be identified as those emitted by nitrogen and oxygen. The most noticeable bright line in the spectrum of the aurora is the famous 'auroral green line' having a wavelength of 5577 Å. This line is easily seen with the aid of a small spectroscope on any night when there is even a faint aurora. (The reader who lives near a town whose roads are lit by mercury lamps is warned against thinking that he can see the aurora every night! What he will probably be seeing is the reflected light of the mercury lamps whose spectrum shows another bright line at 5461 Å—rather nearer the blue end of the spectrum than the auroral line at 5577 Å.) For a long time the origin of the green auroral line was unknown and several rather fantastic suggestions were made as to its origin, but it is now known to be emitted by atomic oxygen. The reason why it could not be produced in the laboratory for several years after its discovery in the aurora is that, before this line is emitted, the displaced electron remains rather a long time (of the order of a second) in its displaced position before returning towards its normal position when it emits light of this particular wavelength. If the oxygen is contained in a vessel—as must be the case in the laboratory—the 'excited' atoms will almost certainly hit the walls of the vessel before they have time to radiate. In the upper atmosphere there are no walls and the atoms can remain 'excited' sufficiently long to allow them to emit their characteristic radiation.

There are several other bright lines and bands in the spectrum of the aurora, including bands due to nitrogen in the violet region and lines due to oxygen at the red end of the spectrum. The human eye cannot distinguish colour when the light is faint (moonlight is only just bright enough to distinguish colours) so that the colours of faint auroras cannot be seen. Bright auroras are frequently coloured and the colours depend on the relative intensities of the different spectral lines present.

(iii) *Light from hydrogen atoms*

The light emitted by hydrogen atoms is of special interest. If most of the light of the aurora comes from oxygen and nitrogen atoms which have been 'excited' by bombardment with hydrogen atoms and electrons from the sun, we might expect that the characteristic wavelengths of hydrogen atoms would also be found in the auroral spectrum. However, the hydrogen atoms shot out from the sun are hydrogen ions with no electrons so that, as we have seen earlier, they cannot emit light until they have acquired an electron, and this they are unlikely to do while they are still moving at a very high speed. It might be thought that as the stream of hydrogen ions and electrons comes over from the sun, some ions and electrons would combine, but the stream of particles is very tenuous and the ions and electrons have little likelihood of colliding on their passage from the sun to the earth. In general the hydrogen ions will only be able to pick up electrons after they have entered the earth's atmosphere, and then only when they have been much slowed down by impacts with molecules of air. The characteristic bright lines emitted by hydrogen have, however, been observed in the light of the aurora, though they are not by any means always present.

(iv) *Speed of the in-coming hydrogen atoms*

If a spectrograph is pointed upwards underneath an auroral arc, in the direction of the earth's total magnetic force, the hydrogen atoms coming in from the sun will be travelling straight towards it, since they are guided by the earth's magnetic field. In this case the lines of the hydrogen spectrum are found to be displaced towards the shorter wavelengths, owing to the high speed of the atoms towards the spectrograph. This change of wavelength, due to the movement of the source—known as the Doppler effect—is found whenever a source of light or sound is moving with a speed comparable with the speed of light or of sound respectively. This displacement of the spectral lines shows that they are not produced by a trace of hydrogen that is normally present in the atmosphere. The speed of the in-coming hydrogen atoms can be found from the difference in wavelength of the hydrogen lines photographed in the aurora and those photographed in the laboratory. The speed of the in-coming hydrogen atoms measured in this way is found to be about 1000 km/s with a maximum of about 3000 km/s, but as we have already pointed out, this will probably be less than that with which they enter the atmosphere. Auroras and magnetic disturbances on the earth tend to occur about a day after the appearance of a solar flare that seems to be associated with the discharge of the particles from the sun. If the particles took 24 h to travel the 150 million km from the sun to the earth, they would have a speed of only about 1700 km/s. But if the hydrogen atoms are to penetrate the atmosphere down to the 100-km level, they must have entered the atmosphere with a speed of about 8000 km/s, in which case they would only have taken about 5 h for their journey from the sun. The reason why they take as long as a day to reach the earth seems to be that they do not come on a direct path but that, on approaching the earth, they are deflected and trapped by the earth's magnetic field. We shall discuss this in a later section.

(v) *Production of different forms of the aurora*

One of the most remarkable things about the aurora is the variety of forms which it may have; quiet arcs extending from horizon to horizon, active rays shooting up to great heights; folded curtains of light, etc. Many of these forms are very narrow in width and we have already seen that even the long arcs may be only a kilometre or so wide and there may be two or more bands running side by side, a short distance apart. If the auroral light is produced by charged particles shot out from the sun, how do these become confined to such narrow bands by the time they reach the earth? Even if the auroral particles come chiefly from the lower parts of the Van Allen belts, at a height of perhaps 10 000 km above the earth, it is still surprising that they arrive in such narrow sheets. We must, of course, remember that the charged particles are guided by the lines of force of the earth's magnetic field and that these lines of force converge downwards towards the earth, so that the electrons travelling downwards will be concentrated in the same way. This effect, however, by no means accounts for the very thin luminous curtains and arcs. Though suggestions have been made to account for the thinness of these auroral sheets, nothing is yet known for certain. The whole question of the interaction of the corpuscular radiation from the sun with the earth's magnetic field will be discussed in the last chapter.

3. SUNLIT AURORAS

A. *Height of Sunlit Auroras*

If photographic measurements of the height of the aurora are made when the sun is only a little below the horizon, the upper part of the atmosphere will still be lit by the sun, though the lower part is in darkness. Under these circumstances the upper parts of the aurora may extend to much greater altitudes than usual. If the measurements are begun only a little after sunset, the heights found at first are about normal—100 to 500 km—but as time goes on, and more and more of the lower atmosphere comes into the shadow, the auroras appear higher and their bases generally lie near the shadow line whatever height this may be, though they may at times extend down into the dark part of the atmosphere. Later on, when the whole of the lower 300 or 400 km of the atmosphere is in shadow, the auroras begin to be seen only at their more normal levels of 100 to 500 km. It is at about this time of transition that some auroral rays may be seen with their tops at about 800 km and extending down to about 100 km, i.e. starting in the high, sunlit atmosphere and passing down into the dark atmosphere. In such cases there is often a break in the rays, or a great diminution in their brightness, near the shadow level. The difference in height between auroras in the sunlit and dark atmosphere is most marked in the case of rays, but the quiet arcs whose bases are usually closely around 100 km when in the dark are found at about 130 km when they are sunlit.

B. *The Cause of the Sunlit Aurora*

Several suggestions have been made to account for the great height of the sunlit aurora. At one time it was thought that the density of the uppermost atmosphere was abnormally increased by the effect of the light pressure of sunlight. When light falls on very small particles or gases it exerts an appreciable pressure on them, and it was suggested that when the sun is very low, and the sunlight passes horizontally through the upper atmosphere, the air at, say, 500 km might be 'blown off', thus temporarily increasing the amount of air at still higher levels. Another suggestion was that at these times the upper atmosphere was expanded by electrical forces. However, it now seems most

likely that the corpuscular radiation from the sun ionizes nitrogen molecules, producing positive nitrogen ions (N_2^+), and that
these ions are very effective in scattering certain wavelengths in
sunlight. The emission of the nitrogen bands in the sunlit
aurora is supposed to be due to two causes. (i) The positive
nitrogen ions may capture an electron and, when this electron
goes towards its normal place on the molecule, it gives out the
light of the nitrogen bands. (ii) When these nitrogen ions are
exposed to sunlight they scatter sunlight of the same wavelengths very efficiently (resonance scattering). Both these processes are supposed to take place in the high, sunlit aurora but,
owing to the very low density of the air at very great heights,
there are relatively few nitrogen ions there and little light is
given out by process (i). However, since process (ii) is very efficient, even the few nitrogen ions can scatter a great deal of sunlight. In the very high atmosphere, therefore, most of the light
is produced by process (ii). Lower down, in the dark part of the
atmosphere, process (ii) cannot take place, but here the density
of the air is much greater and the greater number of nitrogen
ions will allow process (i) to give out more light. Thus in the
highest layers most of the light comes from process (ii) while in
the lower layers it comes only from process (i). One can see that
near the shadow line neither process may give much light, so
that those auroral rays which penetrate the whole of the upper
atmosphere may show a gap around this level.

4. VARIATIONS IN THE FREQUENCY OF THE AURORA AND RELATIONSHIPS WITH SOLAR PHENOMENA

Nearly all the relationships that will be described in Chapter 10
between terrestrial magnetic disturbances and solar phenomena
are also found in the case of the aurora. Large auroral displays
are generally accompanied by large magnetic disturbances and
both show a well-marked cycle of about 11 years—the 11-year
sun-spot cycle—though the maximum of auroral activity seems
to occur a year or two after the sun-spot maximum. There is
evidence that, on the poleward side of each auroral zone,
auroras are seen more frequently at the time of sun-spot
minimum than at sun-spot maximum. Again, like large magnetic
disturbances, bright auroras show a seasonal variation, with

maxima in spring and autumn and a minimum in winter. Though daylight may make observations of the aurora difficult in summer, radio observations of the aurora indicate a summer minimum also. As with magnetic disturbances, the reason for this seasonal variation is not certain. There is also evidence of a 27-day period in the auroral activity—the 27-day rotation period of the sun. It has been suggested that at the time of sun-spot maximum the auroral zones expand and move nearer to the equator. Such an expansion of the auroral zone could account for the maximum auroral frequency at sun-spot maximum that is observed at places outside the auroral zones. It would also account for the minimum auroral frequency that has been thought to occur on the poleward side of the auroral zones at times of sun-spot maximum.

5. OBSERVATIONS OF THE AURORA BY RADAR

One might naturally expect that there would be patches of ionized air associated with the aurora, and that radio waves might be scattered by these patches so that the aurora could be observed on the radar screen. This is found to be the case. The ionization that is produced by the auroral particles apparently consists of columns of ionization with their long axes lying along the lines of the earth's magnetic force. Radio waves may be scattered by these columns, but only if the radio waves strike them nearly at right angles to their length. Since in the northern hemisphere the magnetic lines of force slope upwards and to the south, the tops of the columns of ionization will also be inclined to the south (see Fig. 9.1). If the aurora is to the north of the radar station as shown at A, it will be possible to receive a direct echo since the ray RA strikes the column A at right angles to its length. On the other hand, no direct echo will be received from the auroral column B since the ray RB does not strike it at right angles. The same will apply to auroras situated to the east or west of the radar station. The above holds good for the very short-wave beams usually used in radar, which are too short to be reflected by the ionosphere. If, however, longer wavelengths are used that are reflected by the ionosphere, it may be possible to receive an echo from the column B by waves that have been reflected by the F region and so strike B at right angles. The paths travelled by the radio beams that give an echo may be quite complicated, with one or more reflections between the *E* and *F* regions or with the ground. However, these complications can be sorted out and this method is proving very useful. Radar has the great advantage of being able to

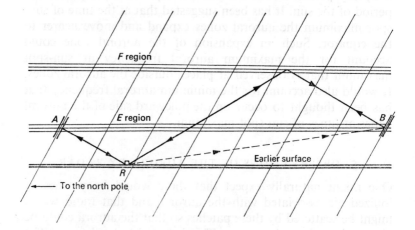

FIG. 9.1. The figure shows diagrammatically how a radar echo can be obtained from a column of auroral ionization *A*, situated in the *E* region to the north of the radar station *R*. An echo can also be obtained from the column of auroral ionization *B* to the south of the radar station, but only if the radio waves are reflected from the *F* region. The uniformly spaced thin sloping lines represent the lines of the earth's magnetic force.

detect the aurora equally well in cloudy and clear weather and in daylight and darkness. Radar measurements have shown that there is a strong diurnal variation in the occurrence of the aurora with a maximum at night and a minimum in the day-time in high magnetic latitudes, while in low latitudes there is small secondary minimum at midnight. Radar observations of the aurora—most of which have so far been made at places outside the auroral belts—confirm the visual observations that the aurora is most frequently seen in spring and autumn and least frequently in winter and summer. The latter minimum cannot, of course, be well observed visually owing to the long hours of daylight in high latitudes. Radar observations also show the 11-year sun-spot period in the frequency of the aurora.

PRODUCTION OF ARTIFICIAL AURORAS

It will be shown that electrically charged particles approaching the earth will be deflected by the earth's magnetic field and will be forced to travel backwards and forwards in spiral paths between points high up in the northern and southern hemispheres. Since even small nuclear explosions produce large numbers of electrons moving at high speeds, if such an explosion was made high in the atmosphere at a suitable latitude, then the artificially produced electrons would be expected to travel in the same way, backwards and forwards between their turning points in the northern and southern hemispheres and rising to great heights above the equator. These electrons would be expected to produce auroral effects, not only near the site of the explosion, but also at the place where they approach the earth in the opposite hemisphere.

In 1958 three small atomic explosions were made in the south Atlantic ocean of latitudes of 38 and 50° S. at a height of about 500 km and the theoretical expectations were remarkably confirmed. In the vicinity of the explosion an aurora was immediately observed extending upwards and downwards along the lines of force of the earth's magnetic field. Not only so, but an aurora was observed, both visually and by radar, at the expected place in the northern hemisphere within a minute of the explosion, although this was several thousand kilometres away and the electrons must have travelled up to a height of some 4000 km before coming down towards the earth again. The presence of the artificial electrons was still detected some hours after the explosion, and it was estimated that they must have travelled some millions of times backwards and forwards between their turning points in the opposite hemispheres before finally being scattered out of their paths by collisions with air molecules. Both the green line (5577 Å) and the nitrogen lines of the natural aurora were visible in these artificial auroras. An even more spectacular aurora was produced by the larger explosion at a great height in the summer of 1962.†

† This also produced a temporary radiation belt below the Van Allen belts.

THE AIRGLOW

I. NATURE OF THE AIRGLOW

On a clear, cloudless, and moonless night, at places well away from artificial lights, there is always enough light from the sky to find one's way about. Some of this light, of course, comes from the visible stars, but the background of sky between the stars provides much of the light. Some of this background light again comes from the multitudes of stars that are too faint to be seen individually by the eye. Some of the light is sunlight that has been scattered by particles in space between the earth and the sun; such light is particularly strong in certain directions and produces the well-known zodiacal light that can easily be detected in the evening sky in spring a few hours after sunset. Two types of observation, however, show that much of the light is neither starlight nor ordinarily scattered sunlight: (i) certain bright lines can be seen in the spectrum of the skylight which are not present in starlight or sunlight; (ii) there is much variation in the brightness of the sky from one night to another. The background light is produced in the upper atmosphere and is known as the airglow. This airglow is extremely faint, but it is bright enough to be of importance to astronomers wishing to photograph very faint objects such as very distant nebulae, since the light fogs the photographic plates during the very long exposures that are necessary. At times it may be sufficiently bright to make the fainter stars difficult to see by eye. Unlike the polar aurora, the airglow is equally visible all over the world, though in high latitudes it may be difficult to tell whether, at any particular time, there is a weak aurora or whether the light comes from the airglow. In lower latitudes where the true aurora is seldom seen there is little confusion between the two. In these places the brightness of the airglow shows no connection with the activity of the aurora as seen in higher latitudes, or with disturbances of the earth's magnetic field with which the aurora is closely connected.

2. THE SPECTRUM OF THE AIRGLOW

Photographing the spectrum of the airglow is even more difficult than photographing the spectrum of the aurora because it is so very faint: long exposures and spectrographs with great light-gathering power must be used, and accurate measurements of the wavelengths of the bright lines found in the spectrum are difficult to make. The first bright line to be found in the spectrum of the airglow was a green line similar to the auroral green line, and it has now been established that it is the same line, i.e. that produced by atomic oxygen with a wavelength of 5577 Å. Most of the other bright lines found in the spectrum of the airglow are also found in the spectrum of the aurora with one remarkable exception, viz. the sodium 'D' lines. It is so surprising that appreciable quantities of sodium should be present in the upper atmosphere, that careful measurements have been made and these confirm that the light is really that of the double sodium 'D' line with wavelengths of 5890 and 5996 Å. In higher latitudes the strength of the sodium 'D' line is increased when the normal aurora is present. The reason for this is not yet known. In addition to these bright lines, the light of the night sky also shows a faint continuous spectrum which is probably scattered sunlight since it shows the well-known, strong *absorption* lines, 'H' and 'K' of calcium, which are so marked a feature of sunlight. The spectrum of the airglow also contains a strong band just outside the visible spectrum, at a wavelength of 10 400 Å. The energy of this radiation is greater than that of the visible part of the spectrum.

3. THE HEIGHT OF THE AIRGLOW

In order to find out at what height in the atmosphere the light of the airglow is emitted, instruments have been sent up on rockets at night to measure the intensity of light coming downwards through the atmosphere. So long as the source of the airglow is above the instrument, the intensity of the light it receives will remain constant as the rocket rises, but as soon as the rocket enters the region where the airglow is produced, the light it receives will begin to fall off, and will fall to zero when the rocket reaches the top of the region where the light is produced. The instruments are provided with optical filters so that the different bright lines in the spectrum of the airglow can be studied separately as well as the faint continuous spectrum. Measurements of this kind have shown that the light of the green auroral line (5577 Å) is emitted at altitudes between 80 and

120 km with a maximum at about 95 km. The light of the yellow sodium lines is emitted by a region some 10 km lower.

4. INJECTION OF SODIUM VAPOUR INTO THE UPPER ATMOSPHERE

If the very small quantity of sodium that is present in the upper atmosphere under natural conditions can give rise to an appreciable amount of light in the airglow, it would be expected that if a few pounds of sodium were carried up by a rocket and vaporized at a height of, say, 90 km, then an intense glow might be produced. In 1955 and 1956 rockets were sent up and discharged sodium vapour into the upper atmosphere during twilight. As was expected, these clouds of sodium vapour glowed brightly and remained visible for some time before diffusing and becoming too thin to give much light.

5. THE CAUSE OF THE AIRGLOW

The increase in the brightness of the airglow that is seen during twilight, when the upper air is still lit by sunlight, is almost certainly scattered sunlight, the scattering being produced by atoms of oxygen, sodium, etc., which are able to scatter certain wavelengths very efficiently. We have already discussed this 'resonance scattering' in the earlier section on sunlit auroras, and the twilight airglow is thought to be produced in much the same way.

The airglow during the night is more difficult to explain. The energy required to produce the glow might come from sunlight that is stored up in some way until the night, or from charged particles entering the atmosphere or even from numerous small meteors. Charged particles would mostly enter the atmosphere in high latitudes, while the airglow is seen all over the world, so that charged particles are unlikely to be a major source of the energy. If the energy comes from sunlight, the production of the airglow at night might be due to either chemical reactions or to ionization. We know that the short wavelengths of sunlight ionize the upper air during the day-time, and as the electrons recombine with positive ions during the night and return to their normal positions within the atoms, they would give out their characteristic wavelengths of light.

On the other hand, we know that oxygen molecules are broken up into oxygen atoms by sunlight during the day-time. During the night recombination might take place in which three oxygen atoms interact to produce a normal oxygen molecule and an excited oxygen atom, which could radiate light of the auroral green line. It has been suggested that excited sodium atoms are produced by the reaction between a molecule of NaO and atomic oxygen, producing a normal oxygen molecule and an excited sodium atom that would then radiate light of the characteristic sodium wavelengths. In the case of the strong infra-red radiation that seems to be radiated by a hydroxyl molecule (OH), one suggestion is that this is produced by a reaction between hydrogen atoms and ozone, giving rise to a normal oxygen molecule and an excited hydroxyl molecule. However, much of this is speculation and little is really known for certain as to how the airglow is produced.

10. The Earth's Magnetic Field and the Upper Atmosphere

1. INTRODUCTION

THE fact that the earth is an enormous magnet has been known for many centuries, and as long ago as the reign of Queen Elizabeth I William Gilbert gave a diagram which showed correctly the general direction of the magnetic field all round the earth. It has also been known for a long time that the magnetic field is not constant; the direction of the compass needle, for example, changes very much over the centuries; at London about 1600 A.D. it pointed some 10° east of geographical north, while about 1800 A.D. it pointed some 25° to the west of north, since when it has been swinging slowly east again. In addition to these large but very slow variations there are others that are much quicker but also much smaller. In our study of the upper atmosphere we shall be concerned only with these small, rapid variations, since they are produced by electric currents flowing in the upper atmosphere, while the cause of the earth's general magnetic field and its very slow variations is to be found within the solid earth. Little is yet known for certain as to how the general magnetic field of the earth is produced or the cause of its slow variations. Before describing the magnetic effects produced by electric currents in the upper atmosphere it may be well to give a brief, general account of the earth's magnetism and the way in which its changes are measured.

2. GENERAL DESCRIPTION OF THE EARTH'S MAGNETIC FIELD

The magnetic field surrounding the earth is very similar to that which would be found if the earth contained a large bar magnet. The axis of such an imaginary magnet would cut the earth's surface in north-west Greenland at about 78·5° N. and 69° W. and at a roughly corresponding place in the Antipodes, passing near, but not quite through, the centre of the earth. Owing to local variations in the magnetic field, the place where the magnetic force is actually vertical (the local magnetic pole) is now situated in north Canada at about 74° N. and 100° W. The position of these magnetic poles varies with time, giving rise to the slow changes that we have already mentioned.

When dealing with phenomena which are controlled by the earth's magnetic field, it is useful to use the magnetic latitude and longitude instead of the geographical latitude and longitude. On this scheme the axis of the general magnetic field of the earth (omitting small irregularities) defines the north and south poles, and the magnetic equator is defined as the circle round the earth where the magnetic field is horizontal, i.e. where the magnetic dip is zero.

A. *Measurements of the Variations in the Earth's Magnetic Field*

In order to measure the small, rapid variations in the earth's magnetic field apparatus on the following lines may be used.

(i) *Declination*

In order to measure changes in the declination (or the angle between the magnetic and geographical north) a small straight bar magnet is hung by a single torsionless thread so that it is quite free to turn in a horizontal plane and is, in fact, a sensitive compass needle. Since the movements that we wish to measure are quite small—seldom exceeding one degree—the movement of the bar magnet is most conveniently recorded by fixing a small mirror to it and reflecting a beam of light off the mirror so that it falls, as a small spot, on slowly moving photographic paper, thus producing a record of the movements of the magnet (see Fig. 10.1).

(ii) *Horizontal magnetic force*

When we wish to measure the magnitude of the force on the compass needle, rather than the direction of that force, we hang up another straight bar magnet, but in this case using two threads so that it is possible to apply a couple, or turning force,

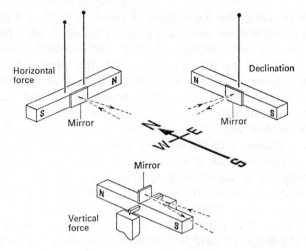

FIG. 10.1. Method of suspending magnets when recording changes in the earth's magnetic field.

The diagram indicates the different methods of suspending small bar magnets in order to record changes in the declination, the horizontal magnetic force, and the vertical magnetic force. Since the movements are very small, mirrors are fixed to the magnets and light is reflected from them on to photographic paper.

to the magnet, and by this means we make the magnet lie east and west instead of north and south, i.e. just at right angles to the direction of the magnetic force acting on it. The couple, or turning force on the bar magnet, produced by the two threads will now be equal to that due to the earth's magnetism. When the magnet is hung in this way, any increase in the horizontal magnetic force will make it turn slightly into the north–south direction against the couple produced by the threads. Similarly a decrease in the magnetic force will allow it to turn slightly in the opposite direction. These small movements are recorded on photographic paper as before.

(iii) *Magnetic 'dip'*

At most places on the earth a bar magnet that is suspended exactly at its centre of gravity, so that it is free to turn in any direction, will not lie in a horizontal plane but one end will dip down; only at the earth's 'magnetic equator' will the magnet lie horizontally. The angle between the horizontal plane and the dipping magnet is known as the magnetic dip. Instead of recording variations in the magnetic dip it is more usual to record variations in the vertical magnetic force. In this case a small bar magnet is supported on knife edges so that it swings in a vertical plane and points to the magnetic north. The magnet is weighted so that it hangs horizontally and any change in the vertical magnetic force causes it to tilt slightly one way or the other.

The small, short-period changes found from records made by apparatus such as that just outlined can be grouped under three headings, and as we shall see, each type has a different cause, though all are connected with the sun and with the upper atmosphere.

(i) On many days the records show only small, fairly regular movements, which tend to recur about the same time each day and generally have only one maximum and one minimum in the day (or at most single subsidiary ones). In the case of the declination, the movements are of the order of a fifth of a degree. Such days are usually known as magnetically 'quiet' days.

(ii) Sometimes much larger, and much less regular, changes are observed, which show no tendency to repeat themselves from day to day and may begin at any time of the day or the night. These changes often begin nearly simultaneously all over the world. Days with such large and irregular changes are known as magnetically disturbed days, and when a disturbance is very large it is called a magnetic storm. During these disturbances the compass needle may vary by as much as a degree or more.

(iii) Occasionally sudden, small changes take place exactly at the time of a solar flare (see Chapter 7) and are generally recorded only at places in the daylight half of the earth. We will now consider each of these three types of variations in more detail.

The methods of recording the earth's magnetic field that were described above, while suitable for routine use at a magnetic observatory on the ground, are clearly quite impracticable for use on aircraft or on satellites, and quite different methods are used. These modern instruments often require rather elaborate electronic equipment. As an example, the proton precession magnetometer uses the spin and magnetic moment of protons (usually in water). After the protons have been polarized by an artificial magnetic field, this field is suddenly removed and the protons oscillate at a frequency which depends on the strength of the earth's magnetic field.

3. SOLAR DIURNAL MAGNETIC VARIATIONS ON 'QUIET DAYS'

If we select a number of days that are magnetically quiet, and plot the average variation of the compass needle through the 24 h, we find a curve such as that shown in Fig. 10.2 for

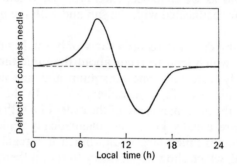

FIG. 10.2. Solar diurnal variation of the magnetic declination on a 'quiet' day.

The curve shows how the compass needle changes direction throughout the 24 h on a typical 'quiet' day. Note that the large movements are confined to the daylight hours. The whole range of movement may be about 10 min of arc.

places in middle northern latitudes; near the equator the changes are smaller and in southern latitudes the direction of the movement of the needle is the opposite to that in northern latitudes. If observations were taken at a place in middle latitudes anywhere round the world a similar curve would be obtained provided that the local time was used, i.e. the changes go with the sun, the north end of the compass needle swinging furthest east a few hours before local noon and furthest west a few hours after local noon. If, instead of the declination, we had taken the values of the horizontal magnetic force or vertical force, we should again have found a regular diurnal variation though, of course, the shape of the curves would have been different from that for the declination. It is important to note that in all cases the changes taking place during the daylight hours are much greater than those occurring during the hours of darkness. It is also found that the changes are larger in summer than in winter.

As long ago as 1882 Balfour Stewart suggested that these magnetic changes might be caused by a regular daily to-and-fro movement of an electrically conducting region situated in the upper atmosphere, such movements being caused by the sun's tidal action or by winds of thermal origin. Movements of an electrically conducting atmosphere across the earth's magnetic field would cause electric currents to flow in the conducting region. These electric currents would themselves cause their own magnetic field, which would be added to the earth's permanent magnetic field and so produce the observed diurnal changes. Electric currents induced in the upper atmosphere by its movement through the permanent magnetic field are similar to those induced in the wires of the moving armature of a dynamo, and for this reason the theory is often known as the dynamo theory. Though the magnetic field of the earth is very small compared to that within a dynamo, yet the total current induced in the upper atmosphere amounts to many thousands of amperes. This theory was put forward long before anything was known about the ionosphere, so that it was the first suggestion that there might be an electrically conducting region in the upper atmosphere such as we now know as the ionosphere.

We have already discussed the ionization of the upper atmosphere fully in Chapter 8 so that we need now only recall that the regular ionization referred to above is due to the action of very short-wave light emitted by the sun. For this reason the ionization is greater by day than by night, and greater in summer than in winter. Pure tidal movements of the air depending on the sun's gravitational attraction would, on the average, be equal by day and by night and would have a 12-hour period, just as the tides in the sea do. However, since the electrical conductivity of the ionosphere is smaller by night than by day, the electric currents that flow during the night will be smaller than those flowing in the daytime although the electric forces producing them will be equally great during the dark and light hours. As a consequence, the movements of the compass needle, for example, are smaller during the hours of darkness than during daylight. It is not yet certain how much of the to-and-fro movement of the air in the ionosphere is due to true tides and how much to winds caused by the heating, and consequent expansion, of the air in the daylight hemisphere.

A. *The 11-year Sun-spot Period*

In Chapter 7 it was shown that the number of sun-spots goes through a marked 11-year period and in Chapter 8 we saw that the ionization of the upper atmosphere also follows the same 11-year period; it might therefore be expected that the range of the diurnal magnetic variations on 'quiet' days would be greater at times of many sun-spots—when the ionosphere is a good conductor—than at times of few sun-spots, when the ionosphere is a worse conductor. This is, indeed, found to be the case and the range of the diurnal variation of magnetic declination on 'quiet' days, for example, follows very closely the curve of sun-spots.

B. *Lunar Diurnal Magnetic Variations*

Both the sun and the moon produce gravitational tides in the atmosphere just as they do in the oceans, and if the dynamo theory is correct we should expect to find lunar diurnal magnetic variations similar to the solar diurnal variations. It is a strong argument for the correctness of the dynamo theory that such lunar variations do exist, since it seems most unlikely that the moon could affect the earth's magnetism except through some gravitational effect such as the tides. It is reasonable to argue that if the lunar tides produce magnetic variations, then the solar tides must do the same. We shall therefore discuss the lunar magnetic variations in a little more detail.

In the oceans the tide due to the moon is greater than that due to the sun, because the moon, though very much smaller than the sun, is much the closer to the earth. In the case of the atmosphere, the tide due to the sun is the larger. This is probably due to the fact that the atmosphere has a natural period of oscillation of almost exactly 12 h, so that it responds more readily to the solar tide of 12 h, than to the lunar tide of about $12\frac{1}{2}$ h. The effect of the solar 12 h tide is readily seen on any barogram taken at a place near the equator, where other variations of pressure are small, and it can be seen on barograms taken in middle latitudes at times when the pressure is steady as in anticyclones. The lunar atmospheric tide is too small to be seen without averaging over a large number of days to remove random variations.

Let us now return to the magnetic variations. If both the sun and the moon produce their own diurnal magnetic variations, their effects will be mixed up together on any one day but they may be separated if a number of days are used and mean values are obtained, either at each solar hour or at each lunar hour. Since the lunar day is about 24 h 50 min by solar time, each lunar hour is longer than a solar hour. At the time of new moon, the moon will be south at the same time as the sun is south, but next day the sun will be south about 50 min earlier than the moon, and so on each day, so that in the course of a month, solar noon will have occurred at all hours by lunar time. If we recorded the deflection of the compass needle at each lunar hour and averaged the values over a month, the effect of the solar diurnal variation would be eliminated and we should be left with the true lunar variation. (In the same way the small lunar diurnal variation is eliminated in the process of finding the average solar diurnal variation from a large number of days.) When this is done we find that there is a small but definite lunar magnetic variation with a range about a tenth that of the solar diurnal variation (see Fig. 10.3). It will be seen that this lunar diurnal variation has two equal maxima and two minima, quite different from the solar diurnal variation. As already pointed out, the mean solar *tide* must have two equal maxima and minima per day, but since the ionosphere is a poor conductor of electricity when not illuminated by the sun, the tidal movements that take place during the hours of darkness cause little electric current to flow and so have little magnetic effect. In the process of averaging out the solar magnetic variation we have also averaged out the solar diurnal variation in the conductivity of the ionosphere, so that we get a lunar magnetic variation that is independent of the varying conductivity of the ionosphere and therefore shows two maxima and two minima. This is just what we should expect from the dynamo theory and is good evidence of its correctness. If we could pick out the magnetic effect of the lunar tide during daylight and compare it with that during the hours of darkness, we should find that the effect was much greater during the daytime than during the night.

We should expect that the increased electrical conductivity of the ionosphere in years of sun-spot maximum would make the range of the lunar diurnal magnetic variation greater in these years than that during years of sun-spot minimum, just as in the case of the solar diurnal variation. However, for some reason which is not yet understood, this is not the case and an

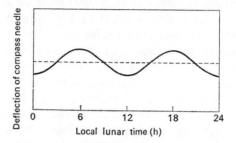

FIG. 10.3. Lunar diurnal variation of magnetic declination.

The curve shows the average change in the direction of the compass needle throughout the lunar day, the solar diurnal changes having been averaged out. The total movement is only about a tenth of that shown in Fig. 10.2. Note that the curve shows two equal maxima and minima.

unexpectedly small effect is found. On the other hand, the range of the lunar variation is much greater in summer than in winter, the difference being larger than in the case of the solar variation.

We would naturally like to know in what part of the ionosphere the electric currents flow that are the cause of the diurnal magnetic variations. Some recent measurements of the earth's magnetic field made at great heights by means of rockets have indicated that the currents flow in the lower part of the E region, probably between 100 and 130 km up. It has been suggested that the currents producing the solar and the lunar variations may flow at different levels, and the fact that the lunar diurnal variations show little connection with the sun-spot cycle may be due to an opposing effect by the currents at the two levels. However, this question can only be settled after much more work has been done.

4. MAGNETIC DISTURBANCE

The recording apparatus such as that described at the beginning of this chapter may continue for some days to produce a smooth trace showing only the regular diurnal changes of 'quiet' days. Then, often quite suddenly, the character of the trace changes; in the case of the horizontal magnetic force, the intensity often increases by a small amount and then, after an hour or so, it falls below its normal value while continuing very irregular. After 1 or 2 days the disturbance gradually dies out and the trace returns to its normal 'quiet' character. Even in large disturbances the compass needle does not usually vary by more than about a degree (except in high latitudes), and the horizontal force does not change by more than a few per cent. It can be shown that the main cause of magnetic disturbances is to be found above the earth's surface as in the case of the 'quiet' day variations.

In contrast to the 'quiet' day variations, which are mainly confined to daylight hours, magnetic disturbances may take place at any time of the day or night. This is because magnetic disturbances are caused by charged particles shot out from the sun and, since the particles carry an electric charge, they are deflected by the magnetic field of the earth and are bent round so that they may fall on either the light or the dark side of the earth. While it can be shown that the main cause of these disturbances lies above the earth's surface, we do not know exactly where the currents flow. They may flow in some part of the ionosphere or they may flow at a still greater distance above the earth in the Van Allen belts which circle the earth (see Chapter 9). While all magnetic disturbances of this type are probably caused by electrically charged particles shot out from the sun, it seems possible to separate the disturbances into two types according to their origin on the sun. In the first type the particles seem to originate in regions near sun-spots or solar flares, while in the second type the 'active' areas cannot be distinguished visually from the rest of the sun's surface, though there is reason for thinking that they avoid areas near sun-spots.

A. *Magnetic Disturbances of the First Type* ('*Sudden Commencements*')

When a solar flare occurs, not only is there a small simultaneous magnetic effect on the earth (which we shall discuss shortly) but a much larger disturbance usually begins about a day later. Such disturbances generally begin suddenly and at the same time all over the earth; hence they are known as sudden commencement disturbances. The largest magnetic disturbances, when the compass needle may move more than one degree, seem to be of this type. Magnetic disturbances of this type show little tendency to recur at intervals of 27 days, as those of the second type do. This would indicate that the 'active' regions on the sun are only short-lived. The smaller disturbances show a marked relation to the 11-year sunspot cycle, very similar to that shown by the range of oscillation of the compass needle on 'quiet' days (see Fig. 10.4). A very curious fact is that there are many more magnetic disturbances in the spring and the autumn than in the winter or summer (see Fig. 10.5). It is of

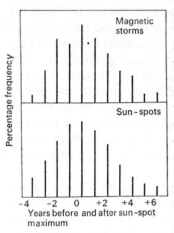

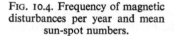

FIG. 10.4. Frequency of magnetic disturbances per year and mean sun-spot numbers.

These magnetic disturbances are of the 'sudden commencement' type.

interest to note that this type of annual variation is also shown by the aurora, if allowance is made for the time during which the aurora could not have been seen because of cloud or of daylight. We cannot imagine that the frequency with which charged particles are shot out from the sun can depend on the position of the earth in its annual orbit round the sun, and indeed the frequency of sun-spots and solar flares shows no such annual variation. No satisfactory explanation for this annual variation has yet been found, for though explanations have been given, they are not free from objections. An obvious suggestion is that magnetic disturbances are more numerous when the earth is immediately opposite one or other of the sun-spot belts on the sun. However, careful study shows that this is not the cause. At the equinoxes the earth's equatorial plane will pass through the sun and, as we have seen in Chapter 9, the Van Allen radiation belts are produced by the trapping of charged particles from the sun by the earth's magnetic field at a great height above the earth. We know that these radiation

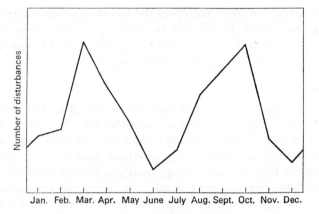

Fig. 10.5. Frequency of large magnetic disturbances at different seasons of the year.

belts are much disturbed and are more intense at times of magnetic disturbance; it is possible that the increased magnetic disturbance at the equinoxes is in some way due to the symmetrical orientation of the earth's magnetic field in relation to the sun at these times.

B. *Magnetic Disturbances of the Second Type*

Turning now to the second type of magnetic disturbance, we find that these disturbances are never very large and do not show the sudden beginning which is a characteristic of the first type. This second type of disturbance shows a strong tendency to recur at intervals of 27 days, which is the period of rotation of the sun as seen from the earth. If on any particular day there is much magnetic disturbance, then on the average, the twenty-seventh day later will also be more than usually disturbed. Similarly, if any day is very quiet then 27 days later the magnetic conditions are likely to be quiet also. This would clearly indicate that magnetic disturbance depends on the condition of the part of the sun which faces the earth and that there are active areas on the sun which persist for more than one solar rotation. These active areas, usually known as *M* regions for want of a better name, cannot be detected by looking at the sun and their existence is inferred from the 27-day recurrence of magnetic effects on the earth. They are quite different from sun-spots and solar flares. The disturbances of the second type show much less connection with the 11-year sun-spot cycle than those of the first type, and such relation as there is tends to show a maximum of disturbance some years after sun-spot maximum.

Polar regions

In very high latitudes, particularly in the region of maximum auroral frequency, magnetic disturbances are much more common than in lower latitudes, and many disturbances found in these high latitudes are not observed nearer to the equator. Indeed in high latitudes, magnetically disturbed conditions are more common than 'quiet' conditions. These polar disturbances seem to be produced by electric currents flowing in the upper atmosphere in the auroral region, and large disturbances are frequently accompanied by bright displays of the aurora.

5. SOLAR FLARES AND THE EARTH'S MAGNETISM

We have already mentioned in Chapter 7 that solar flares emit two quite different types of radiation and these each affect the earth, but in different ways. (i) The very short ultra-violet radiation and X-rays, being a wave type of radiation, travel in straight lines with the speed of light and their effect is to ionize the upper air, so increasing its electrical conductivity. The effect of this type of radiation on the earth will start simultaneously with the visible flare. Moreover, since the radiation travels in straight lines and is not affected by the earth's magnetic field, it will fall on the daylight side of the earth only and no effect will be noticed of flares which occur at night. (ii) Solar flares also emit streams of charged particles—charged atoms and electrons—with speeds which, though very high by ordinary standards, are slower than that of light. The effect of these particles is generally noticed on the earth about a day after the appearance of the flare. Since the particles are electrically charged they are deflected when they move through the earth's magnetic field and may be trapped for a time in the Van Allen radiation belt and then fall on either the dark or the daylight side of the earth; they are, in fact, the same as the particles which we spoke of in the last section under magnetic disturbance. Occasionally, in the case of an exceptionally large flare, the charged particles are shot out with such high speed that they arrive at the earth only quite a short time after the wave-radiation.

On the dynamo theory of the quiet-day diurnal magnetic variation, an increase in the conductivity of the ionosphere would be expected to result in an increase in the electric currents flowing as the result of tidal movements. In Fig. 10.2 we have shown a typical curve of the diurnal variation of the declination. In Fig. 10.6 this curve has been reproduced and,

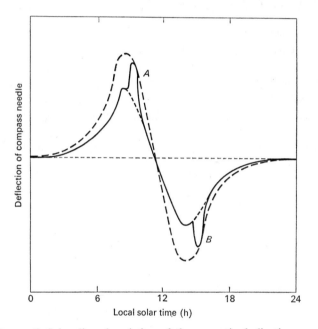

FIG. 10.6. Solar diurnal variation of the magnetic declination on a 'quiet' day together with the effect of solar flare which is supposed to occur at *A* or *B*.

in addition, another similar curve has been added in which the range has been increased by 50 per cent (dotted line). If the compass needle had been following the normal curve of Fig. 10.2 and a solar flare suddenly occurred, resulting in a temporary increase in the conductivity of the ionosphere by 50 per cent, we should expect that the compass needle would immediately begin to follow the second curve with increased range until the effect of the flare died away after an hour or so. Such an effect is shown in Fig. 10.6 at *A* and at *B*. It will be noticed that the direction of the jump in the curve depends on the time of day at which the solar flare happens; if the needle was pointing to the west of its mean position, then the needle will be deflected more to the west, and vice versa. If the flare should happen at a time when the compass needle was nearly in its mean position, then little change will be produced in the declination, though, of course, there may be a change in the horizontal force, or the vertical force.

Future developments

Much work has been done on the way in which charged particles from the sun may cause magnetic disturbances on the earth, but most of this was undertaken before the discovery of the Van Allen radiation belts. The discovery of these belts of charged particles circling the earth is of major importance to the theory of magnetic disturbances, but their discovery is as yet too recent for it to be possible to suggest what the future developments may be.

11. The Magnetosphere and the Van Allen Belts

I. INTRODUCTION

IN the last three chapters we have been considering the iono-sphere, the aurora, and disturbances of the earth's magnetic field, chiefly as observed from the ground. In the present chapter we shall be considering the solar particles that produce these phenomena, mainly as observed in the region between the sun and the earth by means of rockets and earth satellites. The measurements made from rockets, and particularly from artificial earth satellites, during the last few years have opened up a whole new field of knowledge concerning the interaction of the corpus-cular radiation from the sun and the earth's magnetic field. Since the satellites travel round their orbits for many months or years and these orbits gradually change their position in relation to the sun–earth line, instruments carried on satellites are able to measure variations in the solar corpuscular radiation in outer space both with time and with position.

If the earth were isolated in space, its magnetic field would extend out to many times the earth's radius as shown in Fig. 11.1 (a) but become weaker and weaker with increasing distance. In actual fact the earth is not isolated in space, and the con-tinuous stream of corpuscular solar radiation that fills inter-planetary space—the solar wind—greatly modifies the magnetic field at a distance from the earth greater than ten to fifteen earth radii. (Since the distances with which we shall be dealing are rather large, it is convenient to use the radius of the earth as a unit (6370 km).)

The effect of the earth's magnetic field on the solar-charged particles is to deflect them back, away from the earth. In con-sequence there is a reaction on the earth's magnetic field, so that the lines of magnetic force are pressed backwards and do not extend out to very great distances towards the sun. At a distance of ten to fifteen earth radii on the daylight side of the earth there is a region beyond which the magnetic field cannot be detected. This boundary, which is not a sharp one and varies greatly with the time of day and with solar activity, is known as the magneto-pause. The space surrounding the earth within the magnetopause

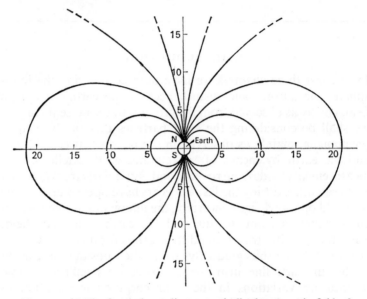

Fig. 11.1 (*a*) The figure shows diagrammatically the magnetic field of the earth as it would be if the earth were isolated in space. The earth is supposed to be viewed from a point on the magnetic equator. Distances are measured in terms of the earth's radius as the unit.

is known as the magnetosphere. As shown in Fig. 11.1 (*b*), the magnetosphere is not a sphere but extends to far greater distances in the direction away from the sun than in that towards the sun. This extension on the night side of the earth is known as the earth's magnetic tail. We will now consider in more detail how all this comes about.

A wire carrying an electric current has a force acting on it if it is in a magnetic field. The direction in which this force tends to push the wire is at right angles both to the direction of the wire and to the direction of the magnetic field, which may be represented by lines of magnetic force. A charged particle moving in a magnetic field will similarly tend to be deflected in a direction at right angles both to its motion and to the field. Let us consider first a charged particle shot out from the sun and coming straight towards the centre of the earth. At a considerable distance from the earth it will begin to encounter the earth's

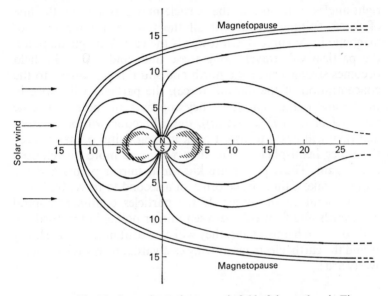

FIG. 11.1 (b). The figure shows the magnetic field of the earth as in Fig. 11 (a) but now allowing for the effect of the solar wind. The double line indicates the magnetopause. The approximate positions of the Van Allen belts are shaded. For simplicity the solar wind is shown as blowing at right angles to the earth's magnetic axis but this angle will vary.

magnetic field, which will here be in a direction parallel to the earth's magnetic north–south axis. Since the particle is moving vertically downwards, it will tend to be deflected into an east–west direction. When the particle has been turned by the magnetic field into an east–west direction and is moving horizontally, it will still be acted on by the field, which will now tend to make it move vertically upwards, so that it will travel away from the earth. If the charged particle is not moving exactly at right angles to the magnetic field, but has a component of velocity in the direction of the field (as will generally be the case), that component of its velocity will not be altered. It is possible that the charged particle may have its path disturbed by collision with another particle and its path so altered that it is trapped by the magnetic field and continues to circle round the line of force. As we have said, the magnetic field exerts no force on the particle in the direction of that field, but only at right angles to it, so that the particle may travel along the line of force, spiralling round it all the time. Since the lines of magnetic force curve down towards the earth's magnetic poles, the particle will travel along these lines and, since the field becomes stronger near the north and south poles (owing to the concentration of the lines of force), the particles will move in tighter and tighter spirals as they approach the poles. At some point (*A* or *C* in Fig. 11.2 (*a*)), their direction will be reversed and they will begin to travel back in their spiral paths towards the other hemisphere. Here they will once more be reflected back again. These points are known as mirror points and the particles take a time of the order of a second to travel from one mirror point to the other. If the particles continue to spiral backwards and forwards between mirror points in the northern and southern hemispheres, they will also drift much more slowly round the earth, electrons moving eastwards and protons moving westwards.

2. THE MAGNETOPAUSE

Artificial earth satellites whose orbits bring them both near the earth and also take them far out into space, can be used to locate the position of the magnetopause. The instruments carried on the satellites measure both the strength of the magnetic field and also the direction of the field. It is found that on the daylight side of the earth the intensity of the magnetic field at first falls off steadily with increasing distance from the earth, but at some distance, usually about ten to fifteen earth radii, it falls off rather suddenly. While near the earth the direction of the magnetic field is roughly that shown in Fig. 11.1 (*b*), further out, beyond where the intensity of the field has fallen suddenly, the direction becomes quite erratic and no longer has any relation to the earth's magnetic field. Outside the magnetopause there are weak fields but these are produced by the highly conducting solar wind. The magnetopause is not a sharp boundary but a region of some thickness and its position and shape vary with solar activity. Just inside the magnetopause the intensity of the earth's magnetic field is about 1/10 000 of that at the surface of the earth. While there are not yet enough measurements to fix the position of the magnetopause in all directions and under all conditions, its general shape is roughly that shown in Fig. 11.1 (b). It is still uncertain whether there is any real magnetopause in the direction of the magnetic tail or whether the tail is 'open'. The direction of the magnetic field in the tail is peculiar and entirely different from that shown in Fig. 11.1 (a). It will be seen in Fig. 11.1 (b) that in the direction of the tail and at distances greater than about twenty earth radii, the lines of magnetic force originating in the northern and the southern hemispheres run nearly parallel to each other, but they are directed in opposite ways. Near the axis of the magnetic tail there is little or no magnetic force. It has been shown by satellites travelling in this region that there is a rather sudden reversal of the direction of magnetic force on crossing the axis of the tail.

The angle at which the charged particles spiral round the lines of magnetic force is important in determining their future history. If the particles move round in a very tight spiral they will be deflected back to the opposite hemisphere as already described, and if they suffer no collisions with other particles they may continue moving between the two hemispheres for a long time. At the same time they will drift round the earth to east or west according to their charge. However, if the particles are moving in a very open spiral, that is more or less along the lines of force, they will not be reflected back but will enter the atmosphere and be stopped by the air molecules. It will be noted that such particles come into the atmosphere at about the auroral zone and it may be these particles which cause the aurora.

3. THE VAN ALLEN RADIATION BELTS

In addition to the great number of charged particles travelling north and south in the space within several earth radii, there are two regions where the concentration of particles is particularly great. These are known as the inner and outer Van

Allen belts and were first discovered by Van Allen in 1958. The instruments that were carried on the early satellites were designed to measure high-speed charged particles—protons and electrons. On rising above the atmosphere they indicated the presence of cosmic rays and particles coming from the sun, as was expected. However, above a certain height the number of charged particles was found to be much greater than was expected. Further measurements have shown that, in the case of those satellites that travelled outwards above low terrestrial latitudes, the number of particles counted increases very rapidly at a height of about 2000 km above the surface of the earth, reaching a maximum at about 4000 km. Here there may be as many as a hundred million particles passing through each square centimetre per second. At rather greater heights there is a small decrease in the number of particles, but the number increases again at still greater heights, reaching a maximum at a distance of about four earth radii. After this the number of particles falls off slowly.

Although they are not sharply divided into two separate belts, the inner and outer regions have different properties. Thus the inner region contains many protons whose numbers change little with time. In the outer region the electrons vary greatly in numbers. The inner belt is mainly confined to geomagnetic latitudes between 30° N. and 30° S., but the outer belt, as indicated in Fig. 11.2 (b), extends over a much wider range of latitudes and dips down towards the earth near the magnetic poles. The inner belt is not the same distance from the earth's geographical axis all the way round the earth, but it is at the same distance from the earth's magnetic axis. There is an anomaly in the earth's magnetic field over the South Atlantic Ocean, the field being locally weaker than normal, and the inner radiation belt comes abnormally low in this region. This shows how closely the radiation belts are governed by the earth's magnetic field.

As already stated, it is not at all clear how the electrons and protons become trapped in the Van Allen belts or what was their immediate previous history. It has been suggested that the protons in the inner belt are produced by the action of cosmic rays on the outer atmosphere. The rate at which protons could be produced in this way is known and it appears that each

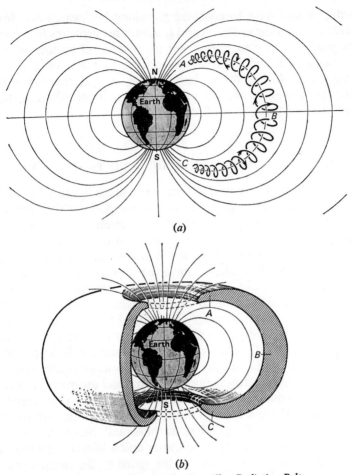

(a)

(b)

FIG. 11.2. *Structure of the Van Allen Radiation Belts*

(a) The figure shows the structure of the belts in a diagrammatic manner only. The Earth's magnetic field is shown by the lines of magnetic force. The path of a charged particle, trapped by the Earth's magnetic field, is shown spiralling around the line of force ABC. The particle may travel back and forth between A and C many times before being scattered out of the belt. There will be multitudes of other particles on similar spiral paths, both nearer and farther from the Earth.

(b) This figure gives a 'cut-away' picture of the band of spiralling particles extending all round the Earth. At ABC a cross-section is shown of the region of maximum density of particles. This is the same as ABC in Fig. 11.2 (a). There is also another radiation belt nearer the Earth which has been omitted from the picture to save confusion.

proton would have to continue travelling backwards and forwards between the northern and southern hemispheres for about
100 years, in order to account for the number of protons which
are actually found. It seems surprising that a proton could
remain undisturbed for so long a time, so that there may be
other processes, at present unknown, which contribute to the
formation of these belts of ionization.

4. CORPUSCULAR RADIATION AND THE AURORA

The light from the normal aurora is produced by the bombardment of air molecules by electrons having speeds of the order of
50 000 to 100 000 km/s. (Note that the electrons in the solar wind
have speeds of the order of 500 km/s and that these would be
stopped by the atmosphere much above the auroral level.)
These high-speed electrons have been actually detected by
instruments on rockets sent up into the visible aurora. It is a
matter of much interest to find out where these high-speed
electrons come from. Are they discharged from the upper Van
Allen belt where it dips down towards the atmosphere above the
auroral zones? This seems rather unlikely since it is found that
the upper Van Allen belt generally contains more electrons than
usual immediately after magnetic storms and auroras. They do
not seem to come directly from the sun, since, at their speeds,
they would take less than an hour to travel from the sun to the
earth, while it is found that auroras and magnetic storms
generally occur about 2 to 3 days after an outburst on the sun. If
they came over from the sun at the speed of the normal solar
wind, how do they become accelerated up to speeds of 50 000
km/s and more by the time they enter the auroral region? The
fact that the particles which produce the aurora do travel backwards and forwards along the lines of force of the earth's
magnetic field between one hemisphere and the other, is suggested by the fact that there is a close similarity between the
changes in the aurora as seen simultaneously at two points in
the northern and southern hemispheres, which are at opposite
ends of the same line of magnetic force. Once an electron has
entered the atmosphere it will be stopped by collisions with air
molecules.

5. CORPUSCULAR RADIATION AND DISTURBANCES OF THE EARTH'S MAGNETIC FIELD

It was pointed out in Chapter 10 that magnetic disturbances on the earth can be divided into two classes:

1. Those that usually take place a day or two after a solar flare and begin with a sudden increase in the horizontal magnetic force, the sudden increase occurring almost simultaneously all over the world. These storms show little tendency to recur at intervals of 27 days—the period of solar rotation.

2. The second type of disturbance is usually smaller, begins gradually, and shows a distinct tendency to recur at intervals of 27 days.

The solar flares that produce the first type of magnetic storm may occur to the east or west of the centre of the visible disc of the sun, though those flares which occur nearly centrally, more often produce magnetic storms. It would seem that these flares send out a great cloud of charged particles which spread out over a wide angle. When this cloud of particles, which must have a fairly sharp front, comes into the region of the earth's magnetic field it causes the sudden beginning of the magnetic disturbance. The charged particles are deflected by the earth's magnetic field and produce a great electric current circulating round the earth, possibly near the magnetopause.

In the second, recurring, type of storm, the solar particles must be emitted more in the form of a jet than a cloud. This jet will rotate with the sun and when it sweeps across the earth it causes the magnetic disturbance. At the present time the area on the sun at which such a jet originates has not been located (the M regions mentioned in Chapter 10), but they must continue to emit the jet of particles for several weeks, since they cause the recurrent storms on the earth. An increase in the number of charged particles has been detected by satellites in the space between the sun and the earth at times of magnetic disturbance, and the temperature of the thermosphere shows a well-marked 27-day period.

EPILOGUE

We have now finished this brief review of research on the atmosphere. Though much has been found out, much still remains to be discovered, but progress has been rapid in recent years. Hardly any of this book could have been written fifty years ago when the writer began work in geophysics. With the many new facilities now becoming available, it is probable that progress will be still more rapid in the future.

We have tried in this book, not only to give an account of some of the more interesting features of the atmosphere, but also to convey something of the interest felt by those taking an active part in these researches and it is hoped that the reader may have caught something of this spirit.

Index

PRINTED IN GREAT BRITAIN
AT THE UNIVERSITY PRESS, OXFORD
BY VIVIAN RIDLER
PRINTER TO THE UNIVERSITY